The Bible to Quit Smoking and Drinking Instantly [3 Books in 1]

Move Beyond Addiction, Regain Immediate Control of Your Decisions, and Invest in Your Health with this Comprehensive Book

Allison Alcantara

ALLISON ALCANTARA

"THE REVOLUTIONARY METHODS FOR ADDICTIONS"

Allison Alcantara has been a heavy smoker for over 30 years. In 1983, after countless failed attempts to quit, she went from 60-100 cigarettes a day to zero without suffering from withdrawal, without using willpower, and without gaining weight. She realized she had discovered what the world was waiting for, the easiest way to quit smoking, and she embarked on a mission to help cure the smokers of the world.

As a result of the phenomenal success of her method, she has earned a reputation as a "Cigarette Killer" and has become a worldwide expert on quitting smoking.

Allison Alcantara's "Spit-Out-It" Method has been successfully applied to a number of problems including sugar addiction, alcohol, debt, and other addictions.

Contents

The Life-Support Guide to Quit Smoking

Introduction 10

Effects of nicotine 16

9+1 Guides to quit smoking 26

1. Cutting down to quit 28

2. Cold turkey 33

3. Nicotine Gum 39

4. Nicotine Lozenge 45

5. Transdermal Patch Bupropion Sustained
   Release (SR) 48

6. Varenicline 51

7. Taking non nicotine medications 55

8. Web-based/On-line Support 65

9. Quit Line 68

10. Support Groups 72

Conclusion: 75

The Life-Support Guide to Quit Drinking

Introduction 80

Why do People drink Alcohol? 82

Effects of Alcohol on Your Body 86

What is Alcoholism 92

Types of Alcoholism 95

Causes of Alcoholism 101

Alcoholism Risk Factors 106

The Disease of Addiction 110

Why People Relapse? 112

9+1 Way to Quit drinking 114

1. Work out a plan 114

2. Talk about it 117

3. Change your environment 120

4. Make time for self-care 123

5. Reach out for support 127

6. Drinking non-alcoholic drinks 128

7. Make the most out of your hangover-free
    mornings 130

8. Build up your motivation to change 133

9. Using Natural remedies to quit
    drinking 134

10. Don't Give Up 138

Conclusion 139

Quit Drinking for Women

Prologue 146

What you should know about Alcohol 148

What are the different drinking levels? 148

When is moderate drinking still too much? 149

How Long Does Alcohol Stay In The Body? 150

What is a standard drink? 151

How do you know how much alcohol is in your drink? 151

Women and Alcohol 152

WEEK ONE 156

Day ONE 157

Day TWO 163

Day THREE 166

Day FOUR 169

Day FIVE 172

Day Six 174

Day Seven 178

WEEK TWO 180

DAY EIGHT AND NINE 182

Day Ten and Eleven 185

Day Twelve and Thirteen..187

Day Fourteen 189

WEEK THREE..193

    DAY FIFTEEN TO TWENTY-ONE.......................................196

WEEK FOUR..200

    DAY TWENTY-TWO TO TWENTY-FOUR 206

    DAY TWENTY-FIVE AND TWENTY-SIX...........................211

    DAY TWENTY-SEVEN AND TWENTY-EIGHT 216

    Epilogue 219

The Life-Support Guide to Quit Smoking

Discover the 9+1 Foolproof Remedies to Free Yourself from Nicotine, Cigarettes and Vapor Cigarettes Once for All!

Allison Alcantara

Contents

Introduction 10

Effects of nicotine 16

9+1 Guides to quit smoking 26

1. Cutting down to quit 28

2. Cold turkey 33

3. Nicotine Gum 39

4. Nicotine Lozenge 45

5. Transdermal Patch Bupropion Sustained
    Release (SR) 48

6. Varenicline 51

7. Taking non nicotine medications 55

8. Web-based/On-line Support 65

9. Quit Line 68

10. Support Groups 72

Conclusion: 75

Introduction

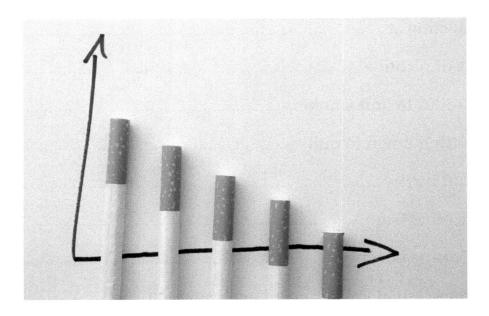

Around 6 trillion cigarettes are smoked worldwide every year .Although by and large utilization has declined marginally in the course of recent years, the future way of worldwide tobacco control is as yet dubious. Regardless of the logical responsibility of some in the tobacco business towards smoking world, all significant tobacco organizations proceed to forcefully publicize cigarettes and overwhelmingly battle tobacco control endeavors around the globe. The critical decreases in smoking rates in the United Kingdom, Australia, Brazil, and different nations that have executed the most developed tobacco control laws internationally are as a rule balance by the expanding utilization in numerous nations with more fragile tobacco control guidelines.

For a large part of the twentieth century, smoking was viewed as a socially scholarly propensity and as an individual decision. It is just in the previous decade or with the goal that the major part of nicotine in supporting smoking conduct has started to be all the more broadly acknowledged. It is currently perceived that cigarette smoking is essentially an appearance of nicotine enslavement and that smokers have independently trademark inclinations for their degree of nicotine admission. Smokers direct the manner in which they puff and breathe in to accomplish their ideal nicotine portion.

The connection with nicotine compulsion doesn't suggest that pharmacological elements drive smoking conduct in a basic manner and to the avoidance of different impacts. Social, monetary, individual, and political impacts all have a significant influence in deciding examples of smoking predominance and end. In spite of the fact that medication impacts support the conduct, family and more extensive social impacts are regularly basic in figuring out who starts smoking, who surrenders, and who proceeds.

Why do people smoke?

The vast majority who smoke began smoking when they were youngsters. The individuals who have companions and additionally guardians who smoke are bound to begin smoking than the individuals who don't. A few teens say that they "simply needed to attempt it," or they thought it was "cool" to smoke.

The tobacco business' advertisements, value breaks, and different advancements for its items are a major impact in our general public. The tobacco and smoking business burns through billions of dollars every year to make and market promotions that show smoking as energizing, impressive, and safe. Tobacco use is additionally appeared in computer games, on the web, and on TV. What's more, motion pictures showing individuals smoking are another huge impact. Studies show that youngsters who see smoking in motion pictures are bound to begin smoking.

A fresher impact on tobacco use is the e-cigarette and other cutting edge, in vogue electronic "vamping" gadgets. Frequently wrongly seen as innocuous as and simpler to get and use than customary tobacco items, these gadgets are a route for new clients to figure out how to breathe in and get dependent on nicotine, which can set them up for smoking.

Trying different things with smoking normally happens in the early teen years and is driven overwhelmingly by psychosocial intentions. For a fledgling, smoking a cigarette is a representative demonstration passing on messages, for example, in the expressions of the tobacco organization Philip Morris, "I'm not, at this point my mom's youngster," and "I'm intense." Children who are pulled in to this juvenile declaration of saw adulthood or defiance will in general come from foundations that favor smoking (for instance, with undeniable degrees of smoking in guardians, kin, and companions; moderately denied neighborhoods; schools where smoking is normal). They likewise tend not to be prevailing as per their own or society's terms (for instance, they have low confidence, have disabled mental prosperity, are overweight, or are helpless achievers at school).

The ideal picture is adequate for the beginner smoker to endure the revolution of the initial not many cigarettes, after which pharmacological components accept a lot more prominent significance. Again in the expressions of Philip Morris, "as the power from the psychosocial imagery dies down, the pharmacological impact takes over to support the propensity." Within a year or so of beginning to smoke, kids breathe in a similar measure of nicotine per cigarette as grown-ups, experience desiring for cigarettes when they can't smoke, make endeavors to stop, and report encountering the entire scope of nicotine withdrawal manifestations.

Any individual who starts utilizing tobacco can get dependent on nicotine. Studies show that smoking is well on the way to turn into a propensity during the adolescent years. The more young and youthful you are when you start to smoke, the almost certain you are to get dependent on nicotine.

As indicated by a report almost 9 out of 10 grown-ups who smoke began before age 18, and essentially completely began by age 26. The report gauges that around 3 out of 4 secondary school smokers will become grown-up smokers regardless of whether they mean to stop in a couple of years.

Enslavement is set apart by the rehashed, impulsive chasing or utilization of a substance notwithstanding its hurtful impacts and undesirable outcomes. Enslavement is mental or passionate reliance on a substance. Nicotine is the known addictive substance in tobacco. Ordinary utilization of tobacco items prompts compulsion in numerous clients. Nicotine is a medication that happens normally in tobacco and it's believed to be just about as addictive as heroin or cocaine.

Effects of nicotine

- Nicotine and different synthetic substances in tobacco smoke are handily assimilated into the blood through the lungs. From that point, nicotine rapidly spreads all through the body.

- At the point when taken in limited quantities, nicotine causes charming emotions and occupies the client from undesirable sentiments. This makes the tobacco client need to utilize more. It follows up on the science of the cerebrum and focal sensory system, influencing temperament. Nicotine works a lot of like other irresistible medications, by flooding the cerebrum's prize circuits with a compound called dopamine. Nicotine additionally gives a tad of an adrenaline surge – adequately not to see, but rather enough to accelerate the heart and raise circulatory strain.

- Nicotine arrives at the cerebrum inside the space of seconds in the wake of enjoying a drag, and its belongings begin to wear off inside a couple of moments. The client may begin to feel aggravated and restless. Generally it doesn't arrive at the purpose of genuine withdrawal side effects; however the individual utilizing the item gets more awkward over the long run. This is the thing that regularly drives the smoker to illuminate once more. Eventually, the individual uses tobacco, the unsavory sentiments disappear, and the cycle proceeds. In the event that the smoker doesn't smoke again soon, withdrawal manifestations deteriorate after some time.

- As the body adjusts to nicotine, individuals who use it will in general build the measure of tobacco they use. This raises the measure of nicotine in their blood, and more tobacco is expected to get a similar impact. This is called resistance. Over the long haul, a specific nicotine level is reached and the individual should keep up the utilization to keep the degree of nicotine inside an agreeable reach.

- Individuals who smoke can immediately get reliant on nicotine and endure physical and enthusiastic (mental or mental) withdrawal manifestations when they quit smoking. These manifestations incorporate crabbiness, anxiety, cerebral pains, and inconvenience dozing. The genuine characteristic of habit, however, is that individuals actually smoke despite the fact that they realize smoking is awful for them – influencing their lives, their wellbeing, and their families' unhealthily. Indeed, a great many people who smoke need to stop.

The following figure shows Arterial and venous levels of nicotine during cigarette smoking.

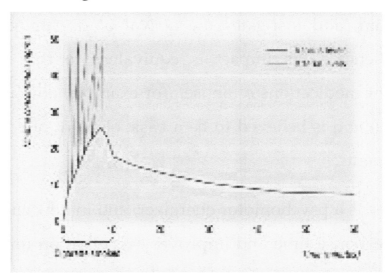

Physical and psychological effects of nicotine

Retention of tobacco smoke from the lung is quick and complete, creating with every inward breath a high focus blood vessel bolus of nicotine that arrives at the cerebrum inside 10-16 seconds, quicker than by intravenous infusion. Nicotine has a distributional half existence of 15-20 minutes and a terminal half-life in blood of two hours. Smokers in this manner experience an example of dreary and transient high blood nicotine focuses from every cigarette, with customary hourly cigarettes expected to keep up raised fixations, and overnight blood levels dropping to near those of non-smokers.

Nicotine slowly affects mind neurochemistry. It enacts nicotinic acetylcholine receptors (nAchRs), which are broadly dispersed in the mind, and instigates the arrival of dopamine in the core accumbency. This impact is equivalent to that delivered by different medications of abuse, (for example, amphetamines and cocaine) and is believed to be a basic element of cerebrum habit instruments.

Nicotine is a psychomotor energizer, and in new clients it speeds basic response time and improves execution on undertakings of supported consideration. Notwithstanding, resistance to large numbers of these impacts before long creates, and constant clients presumably don't keep on getting outright enhancements in execution, psychological handling, or temperament. Smokers commonly report that cigarettes quiet them down when they are focused and assist them with concentrating and work all the more successfully, yet little proof exists that nicotine gives compelling self-prescription to unfriendly disposition states or for adapting to pressure.

The following figure shows the pathways of nicotine reinforcement and addiction.

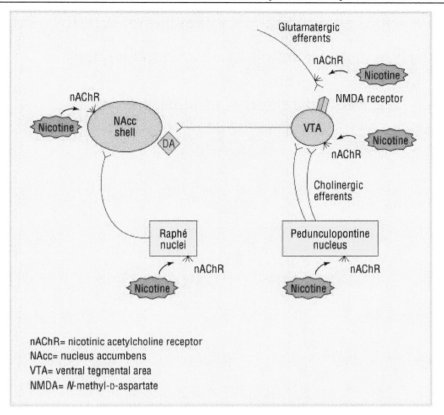

Symptoms of nicotine withdrawal

A significant part of the immovability of cigarette smoking is thought to come from the issues of withdrawal manifestations especially crabbiness, fretfulness, feeling hopeless, impeded fixation, and expanded hunger just as from desires for cigarettes. These withdrawal manifestations start not long after the last cigarette and are at maximal force for the main week. The greater part of the emotional indications at that point resolve more than three or a month, yet craving can endure for a while. Longings, once in a while exceptional, can likewise endure for a long time, particularly whenever set off by situational signals.

Following table shows the effects of nicotine withdrawal.

Symptom	Duration	Incidence (%)
Lightheadedness	< 48 hours	10
Sleep disturbance	< 1 week	25
Poor concentration	< 2 weeks	60
Craving for nicotine	< 2 weeks	70
Irritability or aggression	< 4 weeks	50
Depression	< 4 weeks	60
Restlessness	< 4 weeks	60
Increased appetite	< 10 weeks	70

Regulation of nicotine intake

Smokers show a solid inclination to control their nicotine admissions from cigarettes inside very thin cutoff points. They keep away from admissions that are either excessively low (inciting withdrawal) or excessively high (prompting upsetting impacts of nicotine glut). Inside people, nicotine inclinations arise right off the bat in the smoking vocation and appear to be steady over the long haul. The wonder of nicotine titration is answerable for the disappointment of admissions to decrease in the wake of changing to cigarettes with low tar and nicotine yields. Compensatory puffing and inward breath, working at a psyche level, guarantee that nicotine admissions are kept up.

As nicotine and tar conveyance in smoke are firmly coupled, compensatory smoking similarly keeps up tar admission and annihilations any potential wellbeing acquire from lower tar cigarettes. Comparable compensatory conduct happens in the wake of eliminating the quantity of cigarettes smoked every day; consequently this mainstream technique neglects to convey any important medical advantages.

The figure below shows regulation of nicotine intake; actual and predicted intake per cigarette:

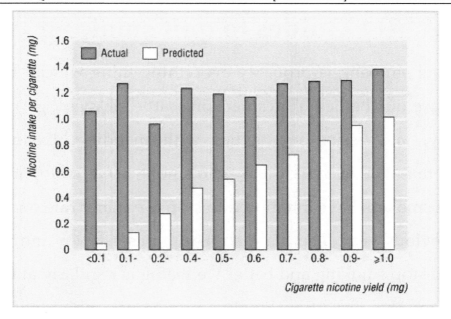

9+1 Guides to quit smoking

Stopping smoking is probably everything thing we can manage to ensure our bodies from infection, battle sickness, go through therapy, and assist our bodies with mending. Examination shows that 70% of individuals who smoke need to stop and that 41% of smokers have attempted to stop for at any rate one day in the previous year. There are so many reasons why individuals need to stop smoking and better wellbeing is regularly at the first spot on the list. Shockingly, numerous individuals who effectively smoke have had stopped many endeavors that were ineffective; this can be debilitating and it can keep individuals from attempting to stop once more.

It may be very hard to tell how to approach stopping smoking, discover the help you need, what's more, and be fruitful in stopping for great. The substance in this part will give you the key data which you need to see how nicotine reliance happens, what happens when you stop nicotine, how to keep away from the upsetting indications of nicotine withdrawal, and most significantly, how to stop smoking securely and viably.

Individuals can stop all alone however it tends to be a test to do this by itself. You will have generally and substantially more achievement in the event that you get backing, advice, and treatment from a medical services proficient or an expert prepared in how to stop smoking. Utilizing nicotine substitution treatment as well as a physician recommended drug to stop in any event duplicates the odds of long haul achievement and at times even quadruples the odds of stopping for great. Following are the ten effective guides to quit smoking:

1. Cutting down to quit

There's no protected degree of cigarette use smoking even a modest quantity can make harm your body. This is the reason there's practically nothing, assuming any, medical advantage from chopping down the quantity of cigarettes you smoke, not at all like stopping completely which has demonstrated medical advantages. Chopping down can, nonetheless, be a decent method to kick you off headed straight toward halting long haul. This is given that you plan well, set the quit date and own it to halting and remaining halted.

While it's in every case best to totally stop smoking on a set date, not every person is prepared to stop straight away. Despite the fact that it's vital to set a quit date inside about a month and a half (shockingly better assuming prior), you can 'slice down to stop' cigarettes over that period, by decreasing the quantity of cigarettes you smoke each day, consistently and fortnight until your quit date.

Well there is some logical proof from enslavement science to back this thought up. Individuals who smoke intensely take in more nicotine and since nicotine is a profoundly addictive substance they will in general need tobacco more and endure all the more sick impacts when they quit utilizing cigarettes.

Unmistakably individuals who smoke less cigarettes experience less withdrawal side effects when they attempt to stop. Looking from a less 'clinical' viewpoint, separating an objective that seems unattainable into little reduced down lumps that appear inside your grip frequently is by all accounts a decent procedure.

The cutting down to quit method involves reducing your smoking as you move towards a quit date.

It's a bit like taking the slow lane you'll still reach your destination, but the journey might seem a little easier.

Cut down to stop may feel ideal for you in the event that you realize you need to stop smoking, however you're not prepared to stop totally at the present time. By chopping down, you're in any event accomplishing something as you move towards a quit date. Exploration shows that smokers who slice down to stop have a comparative possibility of stopping as the individuals who stop suddenly on their picked quit day. Be that you need to set yourself a quit date prior to beginning to chop down as it may. for this to be successful

The benefit of chopping down to stop is that it permits you to decrease your smoking at your own speed, without squeezing yourself as you move towards your quit date. In case you're thinking about utilizing the slice down to stop technique to quit smoking, we prescribe utilizing these systems to assist you with accomplishing your quit objective:

Work out your 'cut down to stop' time-frame:

- Decide how long you will run after your quit day

- Setting a time span of close to 2 a month to lessen to low levels prior to stopping totally appears to work best.

- Be arranged and prepare:

- Avoid circumstances where you used to smoke

- Take up new exercises to supplant old smoking propensities

- Change the schedules you partner with smoking

- Plan rewards utilizing the cash you save from not smoking

- Get uphold on your stopped smoking excursion:

- Ask your friend help you in your quit endeavor.

Presently you've cut directly down, halting totally is only the following short advance. In the event that you decide to step by step cut down the quantity of cigarettes you smoke every prior day halting by and large, you ought to be cautious that:

- You don't start to compensate for smoking less cigarettes by breathing in more profound and enjoying more drags to get a similar nicotine impact

- Attempting an alternate methodology, for example, cutting down over halting totally, may in the drawn out make it harder for you to stop inside and out.

Once in a while cutting down can be counterproductive and takes more responsibility and order than stopping suddenly. You'll actually encounter a similar withdrawal impacts without seeing the monetary and medical advantages of halting totally. On the off chance that you actually don't feel prepared to stop altogether, you could likewise consider options in contrast to smoking, for example, changing to an e-cigarette what cuts down your danger of damage.

2. Cold turkey

Stopping smoking 'immediately' is the point at which you quit smoking unexpectedly, without utilizing any quit smoking items or expert help.

All you use is your own psychological solidarity to stop and battle desires. This psychological strength is otherwise called 'self-control'.

"Without any weaning period" is a handy solution strategy to stopping tobacco, liquor, or medications. As opposed to continuously tightening the substance, you quit taking it right away.

The term comes from the Goosebumps public once in a while get in the days after they quit, which resemble the skin of a "without any weaning period" in the refrigerator.

A few people go without any weaning period since they figure it will be simpler to quit taking the substance immediately than to tighten. They accept they will not be as enticed to utilize the medication or tobacco item in the event that they simply dispose of it.

Be that as it may, without any weaning period may not be the best method to stop particularly for individuals who are subject to a substance. Stopping excessively fast can prompt awkward withdrawal side effects and a ground-breaking desire to begin utilizing the substance once more.

Stopping addictive medications, for example, heroin can be a lot harder immediately. These substances cause actual changes in the cerebrum that lead to serious longings and withdrawal manifestations when you quit taking them.

The security of stopping immediately relies upon the substance you're attempting to stop. Getting off cigarettes or liquor might be protected to do all alone.

Stopping exceptionally addictive medications or an extreme liquor reliance can cause genuine results, and now and again, demise. It's smarter to be under the consideration of a specialist or compulsion treatment focus.

Your cerebrum gets acquainted with addictive medications, for example, narcotics. At the point when you remove its stock excessively fast, you can create seizures, sporadic heart rhythms, and other withdrawal manifestations. A portion of these manifestations can be not kidding or even hazardous.

Undesirable withdrawal manifestations can drive you back into utilizing the substance again to make them stop. Returning to utilizing a medication or liquor after you've quitted is known as a backslide, after you've stopped, your resistance to the substance is brought down. In the event that you do begin to take it once more, you'll be bound to ingest too much.

At the point when individuals quit smoking 'immediately', they ordinarily build up their own strategies and systems. These might include:

- Setting a quit date or stopping precipitously with no earlier arranging
- Utilizing your own regular mental qualities (self-discipline) to beat desires

- To be fruitful however, 'without any weaning period' stopping will as a rule require somewhat seriously arranging, for example,
- Evading circumstances where you used to smoke
- Evaluating new exercises to supplant old smoking propensities
- Changing schedules that you partner with smoking
- Bring upheld on your stopped excursion by a companion or relative
- Putting aside the cash you save from not smoking to remunerate yourself later on.

The main activity whenever you've chosen to stop is to call your primary care physician or medical services supplier. A clinical expert can offer you guidance on the most secure approach to stop.

Your PCP can suggest prescriptions and restoration programs that can help. For instance, they can offer physician endorsed medications to facilitate the longings that accompany stopping smoking or narcotic medications.

Additionally, let your loved ones realize that you want to stop. They can help you through the cycle and divert you in case you're enticed to begin utilizing once more.

Dispose of each enticement. On the off chance that you smoke, toss out all cigarettes, lighters, and ashtrays. In the event that you have liquor use issue, spill out the entirety of the liquor in your cooler and wash room. Take any unused prescriptions to a police headquarters or other approved assortment site.

Likewise plan for desires by have heaps of interruptions close by. Bites like carrot sticks and licorice can keep your hands and mouth involved when you need a cigarette. A decent film may take your brain off the desire to utilize drugs.

At last, line up help. Look for help from an expert advisor or specialist. In case you're thinking about stopping smoking 'immediately', it assists with being readied and has systems set up for additional difficult occasions. Here are a few hints and tips:

- Consider your resolve a muscle – the more you use it, the more grounded it gets! In any case, remember that simply like genuine muscles, your self-control muscle can get drained as well…
- In the event that you feel your determination blurring, help yourself to remember the reasons you needed to turn into a non-smoker and recognize how far you've come.

- Or on the other hand, allow your resolution to recuperate by attempting to maintain a strategic distance from basic clearing triggers or testing out another quit strategy.

Have confidence that over the long haul, your resolve muscle will get more grounded, which means it will get simpler to oversee longings and oppose the craving to smoke.

3. Nicotine Gum

Chewing gum is a shockingly antiquated human conduct, going back at any rate 6,000 years. The antiquated Greeks even bit gum with germicide properties to renew their breath! During the 1980s, scientists thought of the astute thought that gum containing nicotine could help individuals quit smoking.

Nicotine gum is a sort of nicotine substitution treatment (NRT) a gathering of items intended to furnish you with a limited quantity of nicotine, without the tar and other destructive synthetic compounds found in cigarettes.

It's a restoratively demonstrated approach to help you quit smoking, by managing the actual side to your nicotine habit. Along these lines, by proceeding to get low degrees of nicotine subsequent to halting smoking, longings and withdrawal side effects are fundamentally diminished, and individuals frequently locate that this makes the stopping cycle significantly less testing. Subsequently, NRT is perhaps the most well-known approaches to stop, and nicotine gums are both normally utilized and generally accessible as stopped smoking guides.

Nicotine gum is an over-the-counter, sedated biting gum that conveys a portion of nicotine orally. It's expected to supplant the nicotine that individuals would somehow or another get from smoking cigarettes or other tobacco items. While it contains the compound liable for the addictiveness of cigarettes, nicotine gum does exclude any of the other frightful substances. It's additionally sans sugar.

It's an experimentally tried item, and exploration shows that it tends to be extremely successful as a quit smoking guide. Nonetheless, it's essential to take note of that the explanations behind taking up smoking and keeping up the propensity are mind boggling, and the dependence on nicotine is just a single contributor to the issue.

Specialists thusly exhort that nicotine gum ought to be utilized related to treatments that focus on the mental components related with smoking, regardless of whether that is through visiting an advisor, or utilizing a proof based virtual treatment like the Quit Genius application. Nicotine gum ought to be utilized related to treatments that focus on the mental factors related with smoking.

If you are attempting to either stop smoking or cut down on the measure of cigarettes you smoke, nicotine gum could help you on your way. While all nicotine substitution treatment items (gums, patches, tablets and so on) are similarly pretty much as successful as one another, you may wish to go with a gum if your yearnings are abrupt, and you require quick help from your manifestations. The demonstration of biting gum itself can likewise be an interruption from smoking, as it can fulfill the oral obsession that regularly results when you surrender cigarettes.

Prior to beginning nicotine gum treatment, you should visit your PCP or address your drug specialist to guarantee that it's appropriate for you, and that you don't have any ailments which could be undermined by utilizing these items. You'll likewise have to advise your PCP or drug specialist regarding any meds you take, including non-remedy items like nutrient enhancements.

It's particularly significant that pregnant ladies or the individuals who are breastfeeding look for clinical counsel prior to utilizing nicotine gum, to check whether utilizing this prescription will have any unfriendly impacts on your child. This likewise applies to ladies who become pregnant during nicotine gum treatment.

Nicotine gums are accessible in two qualities. The particular nicotine portion that you require relies upon the quantity of cigarettes you're accustomed to smoking. When all is said in done be that as it may, on the off chance that you smoke under 25 cigarettes each day, settle on the gums containing 2mg of nicotine and perceive how you get on. In case you're a weighty smoker, you might be in an ideal situation beginning with the 4mg gum.

You should stand by in any event 15 minutes subsequent to eating or drinking prior to utilizing nicotine gum. Like ordinary gum, this item ought to be bitten, despite the fact that there is somewhat of a procedure needed to guarantee a consistent and complete arrival of nicotine. Rehash this cycle until biting no longer delivers the shivering sensation, implying that all the nicotine has been delivered. This can take up to around 30 minutes.

chew slowly

chew again when the
taste or tingle fades

stop chewing when you
notice a peppery taste
or tingle

park between
cheek & gum

Take care not to swallow the gum and don't bite more than each piece in turn. You can bite up to one piece of gum each hour, so as to decrease the recurrence of utilization as your smoking end program advances. Try not to utilize in excess of 24 pieces in a day.

On the off chance that you miss a portion, don't go through 2 pieces to make for it. Either utilizes a piece of gum when you understand, or basically stand by until the following portion is expected.

Begin utilizing nicotine gum on your quit day, when you'd ordinarily smoke your first cigarette. Nicotine gum is a stopped smoking guide, however it's anything but a drawn out arrangement. Its motivation is to help you battle your habit by making the interaction smoother and simpler to support. While utilizing these items, you're actually conveying an inventory of nicotine into your circulation system, so in the event that you keep on utilizing them uncertainly, you will not have the option to break the actual dependence on nicotine.

All things considered, you'll need to steadily wean yourself off nicotine gum, as both your body and your psyche start to adjust to being without smoke. At the point when you begin utilizing nicotine gum, you should monitor the dates, and work by the accompanying timetable:

- During weeks 1-6: bite 1 piece of gum each 1-2 hours
- During weeks 7-9: bite one piece of gum each 2-4 hours
- During weeks 10-12: bite one piece of gum each 4 to 8 hours

Nicotine gum is a stopped smoking guide, however it's anything but a drawn out arrangement. Nicotine gum isn't intended for delayed use and accordingly shouldn't be utilized for over 12 weeks. On the off chance that you feel that you are as yet battling with nicotine withdrawal indications after the multi week point, look for help from a clinical expert as opposed to proceeding with utilization.

4. Nicotine Lozenge

The nicotine lozenge was presented as an OTC type of nicotine substitution in 2002. It is accessible in 2-mg and 4-mg qualities. The lozenge conveys around 25% more nicotine than the same gum portion. In contrast to the gum, measurement choice depends on the "opportunity to first cigarette" in the wake of waking instead of amount of tobacco use.28 if the primary cigarette is smoked over 1 hour subsequent to waking; the 2-mg structure is a suitable dosing decision. In the event that the principal cigarette is smoked inside 30 minutes of waking, the 4-mg structure ought to be utilized.

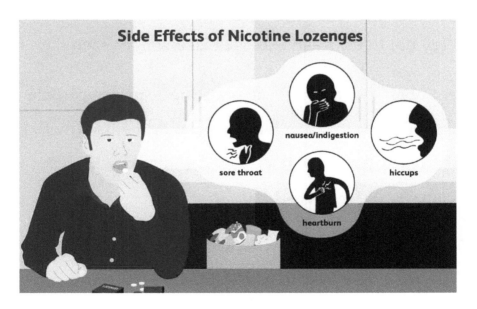

Patients ought to be told not to bite or swallow the lozenge, but rather to move it to various territories of the mouth until it totally breaks down (20 to 30 minutes). Likewise with the gum, utilization of acidic food or drinks 15 minutes prior or during lozenge use will diminish the ingestion of nicotine.

To encourage tightening, urge patients to utilize the lozenge on the accompanying timetable:

- Weeks 1-6: Use 1 lozenge each 1 to 2 hours (use in any event 9 lozenges each day for the initial a month and a half)
- Weeks 7-9: Use 1 lozenge each 2 to 4 hours
- Weeks 10-12: Use 1 lozenge each 4 to 8 hours
- Try not to utilize in excess of 20 lozenges each day

Unintentional swallowing of nicotine can exacerbate active peptic ulcers, and nicotine lozenges should be used with caution in patients with an active history of this disease such as:

- Nausea
- Hiccups
- Cough
- Heartburn
- Headache
- Flatulence

- Insomnia

5. Transdermal Patch Bupropion Sustained Release (SR)

The nicotine transdermal patch is accessible OTC and conveys a consistent portion of nicotine with the most reduced habit capability of all the NRTs. Different transdermal nicotine patch plans are available that fluctuate broadly in detailing, plan, and length of wear (i.e., 16-hour and 24-hour). Plasma nicotine levels got through transdermal conveyance are around half lower than those accomplished with cigarette smoking. Lower levels of nicotine ease the side effects of withdrawal, yet are undeniably more averse to prompt reliance when contrasted and tobacco or different types of NRT.30 Different brands of the transdermal patch have diverse dosing regimens. The clinician should choose the best measurement and routine to address the individual patient's issues. Nicotine patch treatment is utilized to help individuals quit smoking cigarettes. This treatment replaces nicotine in your body that you were getting from cigarettes so you don't have withdrawal indications when you quit smoking.

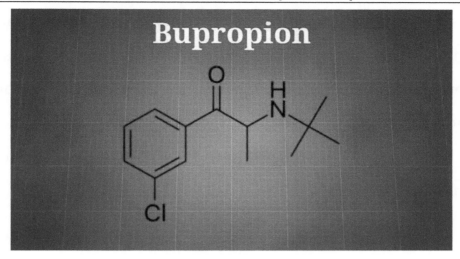

Nicotine patches are applied straightforwardly to the skin. They are applied once every day, as a rule simultaneously every day. Nicotine patches come in different qualities and might be utilized for different periods of time. Follow the bearings on your solution mark cautiously, and ask your essential consideration supplier (PCP) or drug specialist to clarify any part you don't comprehend. Use nicotine skin patches precisely as coordinated. Do not utilize pretty much of them or use them more frequently than endorsed by your PCP.

Prior to utilizing nicotine skin patches, tell your PCP and drug specialist on the off chance that you are oversensitive to sticky tape or any medications. Mention to your PCP and drug specialist what remedy and nonprescription drugs you are taking. Tell your PCP on the off chance that you have or have at any point had a coronary episode, unpredictable pulse, angina, ulcers, uncontrolled hypertension, overactive thyroid, tumor, or a dental condition or turmoil. Tell your PCP in the event that you are pregnant, plan to get pregnant, or are bosom taking care of. In the event that you become pregnant while utilizing nicotine skin patches, call your PCP right away. Nicotine and nicotine skin patches may make hurt the baby.

Albeit results from nicotine skin patches are not normal, they can happen. Tell your PCP if any of these side effects are serious or don't disappear:

- Skin disturbance
- Trouble resting (sleep deprivation)
- tipsiness
- migraine
- furious stomach
- sickness
- regurgitating
- looseness of the bowels
- redness or growing at the patch site

Keep this drug in the holder it came in, firmly shut, and far from youngsters. Store it at room temperature and away from abundance warmth and dampness.

6. Varenicline

Varenicline (trademark Chantix and Champix) is a doctor prescribed medicine used to treat nicotine compulsion. It both lessens needing for and diminishes the pleasurable impacts of cigarettes and other tobacco items. Varenicline causes you quit smoking. To expand your opportunity of accomplishment, utilize this drug with a quit smoking project that incorporates training, backing, and directing. Stopping smoking brings down your danger of heart and lung illness, just as malignant growth. Varenicline works by impeding nicotine's belongings in the cerebrum that make you need to smoke.Discuss the dangers and advantages of this prescription, just as alternate approaches to stop smoking, (for example, nicotine substitution treatment), with your doctor.Varenicline isn't suggested for use by youngsters 16 years or more youthful in light of the fact that it doesn't help this age bunch quit smoking. There are various approaches to utilize varenicline. One path is to marked the calendar to stop smoking prior to starting treatment with this medication. Start taking varenicline as coordinated by your primary care physician, 1 to about fourteen days before the quit date. Take one 0.5-milligram tablet once per day for 3 days, at that point increment to one 0.5-milligram tablet two times every day for 4 days. The portion is gradually expanded to diminish the opportunity of results, (for example, queasiness, irregular dreams). It is alright to smoke during this time. Quit smoking on the quit date. Take the portion recommended by your primary care physician two times every day for the remainder of the treatment time frame (generally 12 weeks).

Another approach to utilize varenicline is to begin taking the medication before you pick a date to stop smoking. Start with the 0.5-milligram tablets and increment the portion as coordinated by your primary care physician. Pick a date to stop smoking that is between days 8 and 35 of treatment. Quit smoking on the date you have picked. Take the portion recommended by your primary care physician for the remainder of the treatment time frame.

In the event that you can't pick a quit date, your primary care physician may guide you to begin taking this medicine and step by step decrease smoking with an objective to stop before the finish of your treatment. Follow your PCP's headings cautiously and decrease smoking as coordinated.

Another approach to utilize varenicline is to begin taking the medication before you pick a date to stop smoking. Start with the 0.5-milligram tablets and increment the portion as coordinated by your primary care physician. Pick a date to stop smoking that is between days 8 and 35 of treatment. Quit smoking on the date you have picked. Take the portion recommended by your primary care physician for the remainder of the treatment time frame.

In the event that you can't pick a quit date, your primary care physician may guide you to begin taking this medicine and step by step decrease smoking with an objective to stop before the finish of your treatment. Follow your PCP's headings cautiously and decrease smoking as coordinated.

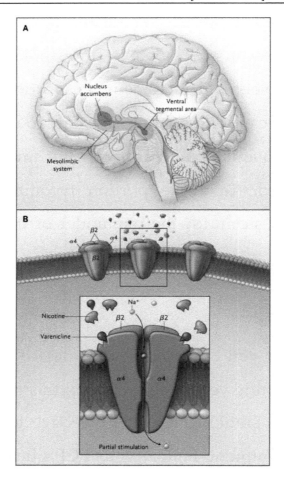

7. Taking non nicotine medications

Most smokers say they need to stop, and around 66% will make an endeavor every year. Notwithstanding, many will decide to make an independent quit endeavor; a technique that has just a little possibility of long haul achievement. The essential motivation behind why numerous smokers think that its hard to stop is a direct result of their reliance on nicotine. Tobacco smoke gives quick conveyance of nicotine to the focal sensory system, where it encourages the arrival of various synapses, for example, dopamine and noradrenaline. In ward smokers, nicotine hardship encourages a withdrawal disorder, comprising of manifestations, for example, fractiousness, low disposition, helpless focus, and inclinations to smoke that can subvert a smokers' endeavor to stop.

Bupropion, an atypical stimulant, is the first, and, up until this point, the solitary non-nicotine treatment authorized for smoking suspension.

There is acceptable reasoning for testing antidepressants for smoking discontinuance, as a solid affiliation exists among smoking and gloom. A higher commonness of smoking exists among individuals who have, or have had a background marked by, despondency. Smokers who are discouraged think that its more hard to stop, a few smokers become discouraged when they quit smoking, and post-end sadness is identified with backslide. Be that as it may, not all antidepressants have been demonstrated to be useful for smoking end.

Bupropion is ventured to help smokers quit through its capacity to restrain the neuronal reuptake of dopamine and noradrenaline, both significant in nicotine reliance and withdrawal. It might likewise help through its activity as a non-serious inhibitor of the nicotinic acetylcholine receptor, and maybe via its impact on serotonin reuptake. Albeit the exact system by which this drug helps smoking suspension stays questionable, bupropion has been demonstrated to expand forbearance rates and lessen the seriousness of withdrawal indications experienced by smokers when they avoid.

Two crucial result contemplates were distributed in the last part of the 1990s. The originally thought about the impact of three distinctive every day portions (100, 150, and 300 mg) with placebo.24 Results showed a straight impact of an expanding portion on point-pervasiveness discontinuance, albeit no huge contrast was found somewhere in the range of 150 and 300 mg each day at a year follow-up. The subsequent significant examination randomized smokers to get either bupropion (300 mg/day), 21 mg/24 h nicotine fix, both bupropion and fix, or placebo.26 The 1-year constant restraint rates were 18%, 10%, 23%, and 6%, individually. All dynamic medicines were altogether in a way that is better than fake treatment, and bupropion was superior to fix alone. There was no additional favorable position of utilizing a mix routine contrasted and bupropion alone.

Since these examinations, various different investigations looking at the viability of bupropion have been distributed. One Cochrane review10 distinguished a sum of 24 that met their incorporation models. Nineteen investigations, which included in excess of 4000 smokers, taken a gander at the viability of bupropion contrasted and fake treatment. All investigations utilized adjunctive conduct uphold. The meta-investigation showed that, contrasted and fake treatment, bupropion around multiplied long haul restraint rates (OR=2.06; 95% CI: 1.77–2.40).

The viability of bupropion has additionally been analyzed in smokers with smoking-related infection, a populace ordinarily more needy and in this manner harder to treat. Individuals with stable cardiovascular infection treated with bupropion, contrasted and fake treatment, accomplished higher 1-year consistent restraint rates (22% versus 9%).29 When utilized in smokers with gentle to direct COPD, bupropion was related with altogether higher forbearance rates at a half year (16% versus 9%)28 however not at 1 year (10% versus 9%).

Its utilization in forestalling smoking backslide has additionally been inspected. The aftereffects of one examination exploring the utilization of bupropion, contrasted and fake treatment, for a year showed no distinction in persistent forbearance rates between bunches at 1 or 2 years subsequent to stopping. Another investigation showed no preferred position of utilizing bupropion over fake treatment for forestalling backslide in patients effectively stopping smoking utilizing a nicotine fix. Hence, proof as of now accessible recommends there is little advantage for utilizing bupropion long haul to forestall backslide.

Hardly any examinations have contrasted bupropion and other smoking-end meds. In one of the essential examinations referenced before, bupropion was more powerful than the nicotine fix. Consolidating NRT and bupropion altogether expanded 1-year result contrasted and fix alone (23% versus

10%). Be that as it may, later examinations have not affirmed these outcomes. Further information are required on this issue.

Bupropion is a protected treatment when utilized effectively. Contraindications ought to be checked while recommending this drug. Moreover, a few insurances should be thought of. Smokers with an inclination to seizures ought not take bupropion except if the advantage of smoking discontinuance exceeds any dangers related with utilizing the medicine. Bupropion, in any case, has been discovered protected to use in smokers with stable cardiovascular sickness, without antagonistic impacts on circulatory strain or pulse.

Nortriptyline is a tricyclic upper that restrains the reuptake of noradrenaline and serotonin. It is attempted to act through its noradrenergic system, lessening the seriousness of withdrawal indications. Different theories for its smoking-end properties incorporate its anxiolytic impacts and anticholinergic results, for example, dry mouth, which may make cigarettes less attractive.

The Cochrane survey recognized six randomized-controlled preliminaries that met their consideration measures. These included preliminaries that contrasted nortriptyline and fake treatment just as consolidating nortriptyline and contrasting it and nicotine fix. Out and out, when pooled, the OR was 2.14 (95% CI: 1.49–3.06). Pooling the outcomes from the four investigations that contrasted nortriptyline and fake treatment just, nortriptyline is found to in any event twofold the possibility of long haul forbearance (OR=2.79; 95% CI: 1.70–4.59). An additional favorable position of nortriptyline is that it is a nonexclusive medicine and cheap.

The treatment routine includes a beginning portion of 25 mg/day, expanding progressively over a time of approximately 3 weeks to an objective portion of 75–100 mg/day, which is by and large expected to arrive at a helpful degree of 50–50 ng/ml.The quit date is normally set once restorative levels of the medication have been reached; this may require 10–28 days. The treatment period is ordinarily 12 weeks, with the portion tightened after this. There is restricted proof of advantage for broadening treatment past 3 months.10

The essential worry with utilizing nortriptyline, as other tricyclic antidepressants, is its unfriendly cardiovascular impacts. It is contraindicated in the individuals who have encountered a new myocardial dead tissue or arrhythmias. Extreme liver infection is another contraindication. Also, there are various precautionary measures to note, for example, use in individuals with cardiovascular sickness, a background marked by epilepsy or psychosis, and ladies who are pregnant or breastfeeding.

Nortriptyline has various regular results (for example dry mouth, dazedness, insecurity, and obscured vision). Urinary maintenance, obstruction, sexual troubles, and seizure hazard are likewise announced. Notwithstanding these, an excess of nortriptyline is ordinarily deadly.

Given that other viable meds for smoking discontinuance are promptly accessible, nortriptyline is presently viewed as a second-line treatment. Besides, it isn't FDA affirmed for smoking end.

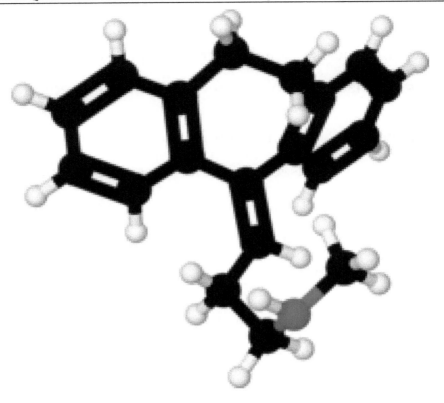

Clonidine has been appeared to improve the manifestations of tobacco withdrawal, and, in certain investigations, increment restraint rates.

The Cochrane survey distinguished a sum of 21 examinations researching its utilization for smoking end. Nonetheless, these were of variable quality, numerous with just present moment follow-up. Just six investigations met the consideration measures, and the pooled results showed an OR of 1.89 (95% CI: 1.30–2.74). This is practically identical with the adequacy of NRT and bupropion Unfortunately, the unfavorable impacts related with this prescription, for example, postural hypotension, unsteadiness and dry mouth, makes its utilization less attractive. Moreover, clonidine causes sedation, albeit this may be of some advantage to the individuals who experience more serious indications of tobacco withdrawal. Gloom, rest aggravation and obstruction are likewise announced, yet these are additionally exemplary indications of nicotine withdrawal, and in this way it is hard to find out which of the two is the causal specialist. Patients with a background marked by sorrow or occlusive fringe vascular infection ought to try not to utilize clonidine.

On the off chance that clonidine is to be utilized for smoking end, at that point treatment ought to be begun 2-3 days prior to stopping, permitting time to arrive at consistent state fixation. It has additionally been utilized in mix with NRT to help oversee withdrawal. Clonidine can be taken orally or through a transdermal fix. Oral portions ordinarily start with 0.1 mg/day, and afterward are slowly expanded, up to 0.4 mg/day. The transdermal portions that have been given are somewhere in the range of 0.1 and 0.3 mg/day. The therapy period is typically short, given over the initial 3 a month subsequent to stopping when withdrawal manifestations are generally serious. After this, the portion is decreased more than a few days, which is especially critical to keep away from hypertensive emergency and hypoglycaemia in individuals with hypertension and diabetes, separately.

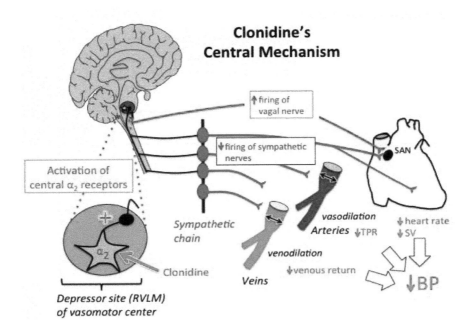

8. Web-based/On-line Support

Existing smoking suspension medicines are tested by low commitment and high backslide rates, proposing the requirement for more inventive, available, and intuitive treatment systems. Twitter is a Web-based stage that permits individuals to speak with one another for the duration of the day utilizing their telephone.

Objective:

This investigation expects to use the online media foundation of Twitter for cultivating shared help to diminish backslide with stopping smoking. Moreover, the examination will look at the impacts of coed versus ladies just gatherings on ladies' prosperity with stopping smoking.

Strategies:

The investigation configuration is a Web-based, three-arm randomized controlled preliminary with two treatment arms (a coed or ladies just Twitter uphold gathering) and a control arm. Members are selected on the web and are randomized to one of the conditions. All members will get two months of blend nicotine substitution treatment (patches in addition to their decision of gum or capsules), sequential messages with connections to Smokefree.gov quit aides, and directions to record their quit date on the web (and to stop smoking on that date) out on the town falling inside seven days of inception of the examination. Members randomized to a treatment arm are set in a completely mechanized Twitter uphold gathering (coed or ladies just), combined with a mate (coordinated on age, sexual orientation, area, and schooling), and urged to speak with the gathering and mate through day by day tweeted conversation subjects and day by day robotized criticism messages (a positive tweet on the off chance that they tweet and an empowering tweet on the off chance that they miss tweeting). Selected online from across the mainland United States, the example comprises of 215 male and 745 female current cigarette smokers needing to stop, matured somewhere in the range of 21 and 59 years. Self-evaluated follow-up reviews are finished online at 1, 3, and a half year after the date they chose to stop smoking, with salivary cotinine approval at 3 and a half year. The essential result is supported biochemically affirmed forbearance at the half year follow-up.

Results: From November 2016 to September 2018, 960 members in 36 gatherings were selected for the randomized controlled preliminary, notwithstanding 20 members in an underlying pilot gathering. Information examination will start soon for the randomized controlled preliminary dependent on information from 896 of the 960 members (93.3%), with 56 members lost to follow-up and 8 dropouts.

Ends:

This examination joins the portable foundation of Twitter with a care group for stopping smoking. Discoveries will illuminate the adequacy regarding virtual distributed care groups for stopping smoking and conceivably clarify sex contrasts in quit rates found in earlier exploration.

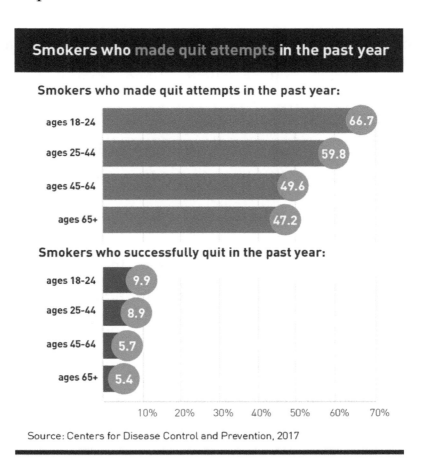

Smokers who made quit attempts in the past year

Smokers who made quit attempts in the past year:

ages 18-24	66.7
ages 25-44	59.8
ages 45-64	49.6
ages 65+	47.2

Smokers who successfully quit in the past year:

ages 18-24	9.9
ages 25-44	8.9
ages 45-64	5.7
ages 65+	5.4

10%   20%   30%   40%   50%   60%   70%

Source: Centers for Disease Control and Prevention, 2017

9. Quit Line

A quitline is a tobacco discontinuance administration accessible through a complementary phone number. Quitlines are staffed by instructors prepared explicitly to help smokers quit. Quitlines convey data, guidance, backing, and references to tobacco clients — paying little heed to their geographic area, race/identity, or monetary status.

Quitlines giving phone guiding to smoking discontinuance get from conduct examination and hypothesis, have been demonstrated to be compelling, and have been received and afterward systematized at both the state and public levels. Despite the fact that analysts have made fundamental commitments to quitline improvement and assessment, this achievement has gone generally unnoticed by the training and exploration networks in clinical, guiding, and wellbeing brain science.

Engineers of a conduct mediation have a fantasy. The substance of their mediation would be gotten from a strong observational and hypothetical establishment. The mediation would be demonstrated to be successful in thorough randomized preliminaries and afterward received by medical care suppliers and frameworks. Following extra corroborative examination, the program would then become systematized, a planned standard help at the nearby, state, or even public level. Scarcely any, conduct programs have accomplished a particularly level of progress. However smoking discontinuance quitlines are moving toward this level.

Quitlines are phone based projects for aiding tobacco clients quit. Tobacco clients start contact with a quitline, and administrations may incorporate sent materials, recorded messages, guiding at the hour of call, callback from an advocate, admittance to suspension drug, or a mix of these administrations. Most administrations are free to the guest.

There are a few favorable circumstances to phone guiding for smoking end. To start with, it is advantageous. Telephone guiding abatements calculated hindrances to treatment and expands administration use. On the off chance that customers need extra assistance over the long run, they can essentially get back to and reconnect in directing. Second, the underlying directing meeting can advance rather rapidly. The semi-mysterious nature of telephone directing encourages genuine conversation, which assists advisors with acquiring an exact clinical picture in a brief timeframe. Third, the phone medium permits guides to give proactive directing (i.e., the instructor calls the customer), in this manner improving the probability that follow-up meetings will happen. Notwithstanding diminishing weakening, proactive advising advances responsibility and social help. Fourth, the phone design fits utilization of an organized directing convention, which gives the base adequate substance to every meeting. An organized convention guarantees that each call is careful yet engaged and brief, making it reasonable for enormous scope application.

Tobacco use is the major, avoidable reason for sickness and passing in the United States, representing 435,000 passings every year . Hence, creating powerful techniques to help tobacco clients quit is in a real sense an immeasurably significant issue. The turn of events and assessment of quitline conventions are an aggregate achievement of numerous specialists, some of them analysts. Albeit the early, original assessment considers were totally distributed in the Journal of Consulting and Clinical Psychology, the vast majority of the resulting work has been distributed in enslavement, clinical, general wellbeing, preventive consideration, or wellbeing training diaries. Theories diaries are not regularly perused by analysts. Quitline intercessions may not be seen as "guiding" or "treatment" by analysts or specialists. Wampold's meaning of psychotherapy is limited to eye to eye cooperations, and California's Board of Psychology doesn't consider phone directing as regulated proficient experience; these hours can't be checked toward licensure. Thus, experts and scientists in clinical, advising, and even wellbeing brain science seem, by all accounts, to be uninformed of quitlines either as an asset for their customers or a chance for their exploration.

10. Support Groups

Gathering guiding can build your opportunity of stopping by 30%. Individuals are animals of propensity — simply ask a smoker who has attempted to stop. But on the other hand were social creatures, and with regards to stopping smoking, individuals around us can have a major effect. Gathering directing may not be pretty much as successful as some different medicines, (for example, drug), yet for individuals searching for the human touch, it tends to be only the thing.

Quitting through gathering treatment or care groups is to build up an arrangement for putting cigarettes behind you and to master abilities for adapting to yearnings — while collaborating (and shocking tales) with other would-be weaklings. "Steady gathering medicines drove by a talented advocate with others stopping simultaneously are powerful," says Jodi Prochaska, PhD, MPH, a clinical clinician and partner educator at the University of California, San Francisco, who works at the universitys Center for Tobacco Control Research and Education.

"Making a guarantee to stop and declaring that obligation to others has been demonstrated to be useful."

Directing and a Nicotine Patch Helped Natasha Quit Smoking

Tobacco use is the major, avoidable reason for ailment and passing in the United States, representing 435,000 passings every year . Hence, creating viable techniques to help tobacco clients quit is in a real sense an incomprehensibly important issue. The turn of events and assessment of quitline conventions are an aggregate achievement of numerous specialists, some of them therapists. Albeit the early, fundamental assessment contemplates were totally distributed in the Journal of Consulting and Clinical Psychology, a large portion of the ensuing work has been distributed in dependence, clinical, general wellbeing, preventive consideration, or wellbeing instruction diaries. Proposals diaries are not normally perused by clinicians. Quitline mediations may not be seen as "advising" or "treatment" by scientists or professionals. Wampold's meaning of psychotherapy is limited to vis-à-vis cooperations, and California's Board of Psychology doesn't consider phone advising as directed proficient experience; these hours can't be checked toward licensure. Subsequently, professionals and analysts in clinical, guiding, and even wellbeing brain science seem, by all accounts, to be ignorant of quitlines either as an asset for their customers or a chance for their exploration.

Conclusion:

Smoking discontinuance lessens hazard for some, unfriendly wellbeing impacts, including regenerative wellbeing results, cardiovascular infections, ongoing obstructive aspiratory sickness, and disease. Stopping smoking is likewise gainful to the individuals who have been determined to have coronary illness and ongoing obstructive pneumonic infection.

Smoking suspension is helpful at whatever stage in life. Smoking end improves wellbeing status and upgrades personal satisfaction.

Smoking suspension diminishes the danger of sudden passing and can add as much as 10 years to future.

Smoking spots a significant monetary weight on smokers, medical services frameworks, and society. Smoking discontinuance lessens this weight, including smoking attributable medical care uses.

Smoking suspension can be expanded by raising the cost of cigarettes, embracing exhaustive smoke free strategies, actualizing broad communications crusades, requiring pictorial wellbeing admonitions, and keeping up extensive statewide tobacco control programs.

Protection inclusion for smoking suspension treatment that is extensive, hindrance free and generally advanced expands the utilization of these treatment administrations, prompts higher paces of fruitful stopping, and is financially savvy. A large proportion of adult smokers report using non-evidence-based approaches when trying to quit smoking, such as switching to other tobacco products.

Counsel from professionals or experts to stop smoking has expanded since 2000; nonetheless, four out of each nine grown-up cigarette smokers who saw health proficient during the previous year didn't get guidance to stop.

The Life-Support Guide to Quit Drinking

The 9+1 Sober Tips on How to Take the Radical Choice to Stop Drinking and Fix Past Mistakes

Allison Alcantara

Contents

Introduction 80

Why do People drink Alcohol? 82

Effects of Alcohol on Your Body 86

What is Alcoholism 92

Types of Alcoholism 95

Causes of Alcoholism 101

Alcoholism Risk Factors 106

The Disease of Addiction 110

Why People Relapse? 112

9+1 Way to Quit drinking 114

1. Work out a plan 114

2. Talk about it 117

3. Change your environment 120

4. Make time for self-care 123

5. Reach out for support 127

6. Drinking non-alcoholic drinks 128

7. Make the most out of your hangover-free
    mornings 130

8. Build up your motivation to change 133

9. Using Natural remedies to quit drinking 134

10. Don't Give Up 138

Conclusion 139

Introduction

Around 2 billion individuals overall devour alcoholic drinks, which can have prompt and long-term consequences on health and social life. More than 76 million people are presently affected by alcohol use disorders, for example, alcohol reliance and abuse. Contingent upon the measure of alcohol consumed and the example of drinking, alcohol consumption can prompt inebriation and alcohol reliance. It can bring about disablement or death from accidents or contribute to depression and suicide. Moreover, it can cause chronic illnesses, for example, cancer and liver disease in individuals who've been drinking heavily for some years.

Alcohol has a toll of 1.8 million deaths every year, which addresses 3.2% of all deaths worldwide. Unexpected wounds represent about 33% of the deaths from alcohol. Alcohol is the third most basic reason for demise in developed nations. In the predetermined number of agricultural nations where mortality is low, alcohol is the main source of illness and sickness.

Damage to human existence is frequently portrayed regarding the loss of "disability-adjusted life-years" (DALYs). This measure considers the quantity of years lost because of unexpected losses just as the years went through living with a disability.

Worldwide, alcohol causes a deficiency of 58.3 million DALYs annually, which addresses 4% of the total loss of DALYs from all causes. Mental disorders and illnesses of the sensory system account for about 40% of DALYs lost due to alcohol.

Why do People drink Alcohol?

For a great many people, a drink or two can be an approach to celebrate an occasion or praise a decent meal. Others may not appreciate alcohol by any stretch of the imagination; they don't care for the taste, they don't care for the vibe of being tipsy, or they don't care for feeling out of control. In case you end up finding a way into these categories, understanding the difficult drinker in your life can be troublesome.

At Origins, we are an organization involved to a great extent of recuperated alcoholics, so we see really well why individuals drink—not just toward the start of their "drinking vocations," however whenever addiction has grabbed hold.

The "Effect Produced"

In the beginning phases of drinking, people frequently find that alcohol creates a scope of lovely effects. These effects are frequently slippery to such an extent that people keep on drinking even after their drinking has become "a problem." Here are a couple of those effects noted by both moderate drinkers and alcoholics the same.

Stress Relief

For both moderate consumers and alcoholics, alcohol has awesome anxiolytic ("anti-anxiety") properties, which means it can restrain anxiety or the sensation of stress. It is a typical path for individuals to loosen up in the wake of a monotonous day's work.

Alcoholics frequently discover this effect from the beginning in their drinking careers. As addiction takes hold, the beset person continues to drink despite evidence that alcohol is done giving any semblance of stress relief. Moved by the delusion that they can stop after a glass or two, they unsuccessfully chase this sensation of relief. As a rule, for the alcoholic, drinking alcohol exacerbates the very stress they were expecting to maintain a strategic distance from.

Peer Pressure and Camaraderie

Numerous people drink when others around them are drinking. Indeed, most non-alcoholics will in general drink in social circumstances, for example, weddings or football games, where alcohol is viewed as a piece of the actual occasion. Despite the fact that the expression "peer pressure" is regularly connected with young people, it isn't restricted to those in middle school, secondary school, or school. Drinking is pervasive in our way of life, socially acknowledged, and lawful. Peer pressure to drinking alcohol can exist at any phase of life.

For the alcoholic, the fixation to drink can transform peer pressure into a cleverly disguised excuse for drinking—in any event, when they realize they shouldn't drink dependent on mounting evidence it's an issue. Regularly, alcoholics accept they are drinking to have a good time and enjoy time with their friends which is strangely unexpected as they as often as a possible drink alone.

To Lose One's Inhibitions

Let's be honest, there are a lot of shy individuals out there. Additionally, there are likewise many circumstances in which somebody doesn't even essentially need to be too shy to be scared. First dates and enormous gatherings loaded up with strangers are common examples. Whatever the explanation, individuals regularly drink alcohol to lose their restraints in these sorts of settings. On account of alcohol's ability to cause individuals to feel great in circumstances where they in any case would not, it is commonly referred to as "liquid courage." For some non-alcoholics, it is an awesome, brief "social lubricant."

Binge drinkers may turn out to be uninhibited to such an extent that they act in an inappropriate, embarrassing, or obnoxious manner. For drunkards who have built up a staggering obsession to drink, this effect can deteriorate relationships and cause untold horror.

Alcohol

- ▶Why do people drink?
    - ▶They may want to fit in with a group.
    - ▶They may want to feel older.
    - ▶They may think it will help them avoid their problems.
    - None of these are healthful reasons.

Effects of Alcohol on Your Body

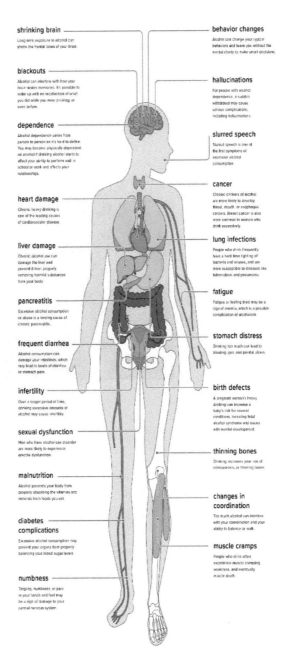

Alcohol's effect on your body begins from the second you take your first taste. While a periodic glass of wine with supper isn't a reason for concern, the combined impacts of drinking wine, lager, or spirits can incur significant damage.

Digestive and endocrine glands

Drinking a lot of alcohol can cause abnormal activation of digestive enzymes created by the pancreas. The development of these enzymes can prompt inflammation known as pancreatitis. Pancreatitis can turn into a drawn-out condition and cause serious intricacies.

Inflammatory damage

The liver is an organ that assists break with bringing down and eliminate harmful substances from your body, including alcohol. Long-term alcohol use meddles with this cycle. It additionally expands your danger for chronic liver inflammation and liver disease. The scarring brought about by this inflammation is known as cirrhosis. The development of scar tissue annihilates the liver. As the liver turns out to be progressively harmed, it has a harder time eliminating toxic substances from your body.

Sugar levels

The pancreas manages your body's insulin use and reaction to glucose. At the point when your pancreas and liver aren't working appropriately, you risk experiencing low blood sugar or hypoglycemia. A harmed pancreas may likewise keep the body from producing sufficient insulin to utilize sugar. This can prompt hyperglycemia or a lot of sugar in the blood.

Central nervous system

As alcohol makes more damage to your central nervous system, you may encounter numbness and tingling sensations in your feet and hands. Drinking additionally makes it hard for your brain to make long-term memories. It likewise lessens your capacity to think clearly and settle on rational decisions. Over the long run, frontal lobe damage can happen. This territory of the brain is answerable for emotional control, short-term memory, and judgment, in addition to other essential jobs.

Digestive system

The association between alcohol utilization and your digestive system probably won't appear to be immediately clear. The side effects frequently just appear after there has been damage. Furthermore, the more you drink, the greater the damage will turn into. Alcohol can damage the tissues in your digestive tract and keep your intestines from processing food and absorbing nutrients and vitamins. Subsequently, malnutrition may happen. Excessive alcohol consumption can cause the following:

- gassiness

- bloating

- a feeling of fullness in abdomen

- diarrhea

Circulatory system

Alcohol can influence your heart and lungs. Individuals who are chronic drinkers of alcohol have a higher danger of heart-related issues than individuals who don't drink. Women who drink are bound to create heart disease than men who drink. Circulatory system complications include:

- High blood pressure

- Irregular heartbeat

- Difficulty pumping blood through the body

- Stroke

- Heart attack

- Heart disease

Sexual and reproductive health

You may figure drinking alcohol can lower your restraints and assist you with having a good time in bed. However, the reality is very unique. Men who drink in excess are more liable to experience erectile dysfunction. Heavy drinking can likewise prevent sex hormone production and lower your libido.

Women who drink a lot may quit menstruating. That puts them in more serious danger for infertility. Women who drink intensely during pregnancy have a higher danger of premature delivery, miscarriage, or stillbirth.

Skeletal and muscle systems

Long haul alcohol use may keep your body from keeping your bones solid. This habit may cause thinner bones and increment your danger for fractures in the event that you fall. And fractures may recuperate more slowly. Drinking alcohol may likewise prompt muscle weakness, cramping, and eventually atrophy.

Immune system

Drinking heavily weakens your body's regular insusceptible framework. This makes it harder for your body to ward off invading germs and infections.

Individuals who drink heavily throughout a long timeframe are additionally more prone to develop pneumonia or tuberculosis than the general population. Around 10% of all tuberculosis cases worldwide can be attached to alcohol consumption.

Drinking alcohol likewise builds your danger for a few kinds of cancer, including mouth, breast, and colon.

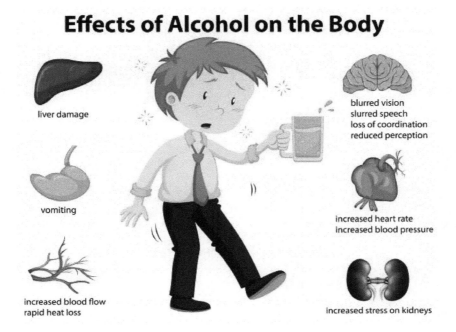

What is Alcoholism

Alcoholism is the most dangerous type of alcohol abuse and includes the inability to manage drinking habits. It is likewise usually alluded to as alcohol use disorder. Alcohol use disorder is coordinated into three classifications: mild, moderate, and severe. Every classification has different symptoms and can cause hurtful side effects. Whenever left untreated, any sort of alcohol abuse can spiral crazy. People battling with alcoholism regularly feel like they can't function typically without alcohol.

This can cause alot issues and affect professional objectives, individual issues, relationships, and by and large wellbeing. Over the long haul, the genuine side effects of predictable alcohol abuse can deteriorate and deliver harmful entanglements.

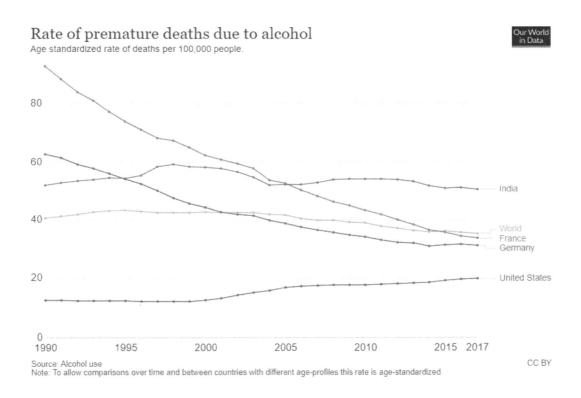

Rate of premature deaths due to alcohol
Age standardized rate of deaths per 100,000 people.

India
World
France
Germany
United States

Source: Alcohol use
Note: To allow comparisons over time and between countries with different age-profiles this rate is age-standardized.

The chart shows alcohol consumption since 1890 out of various countries. Across these high-income countries, the annual average today lies between 5.6 liters in Japan and 10.4 liters in Austria. A century ago, a few countries had a lot higher degree of alcohol consumption. In France, during the 1920s the average was 22.1 liters of pure alcohol per person per year. This equivalents 184 one-liter wine bottles per person per year. Note that as opposed to the cutting edge insights that are communicated in alcohol consumption per person older than 15 years, this incorporates children also – the average alcohol consumption per adult was therefore much higher.

Types of Alcoholism

Various kinds of alcoholics will languish over various reasons. A few gatherings may not understand that their drinking is an issue. Or maybe, it is only a piece of what their identity is. Notwithstanding, regardless of your age, status, or family, alcoholism can make long-term issues that damage your health and relationships, regardless of the subtype. There is a generalization in America of a "typical alcoholic". Nonetheless, an investigation from the National Institute on Alcohol Abuse and Alcoholism (NIAAA), National Institute of Health (NIH), and the National Epidemiological Survey on Alcohol and Related Conditions (NESARC) set out to settle that notion. These organizations conducted a national, clinical investigation got from different examinations on alcoholics. The examination found that there are five subtypes of alcoholics which are the following:

Young Adult Subtype

It is resolved that generally 31.5% of alcoholics fall into youthful grown-ups, which is the biggest single gathering. This gathering will in general start drinking at an early age (around 19) and builds up an alcohol reliance ahead of schedule (around 24). This gathering has nearly low paces of co-happening psychological wellness conditions and moderate paces of other substance misuse issues and relatives with alcoholism. The youthful grown-up subtype is less inclined to make some full-memories work however is bound to be in school than different gatherings.

This gathering is likewise far-fetched at any point to have been hitched. This subtype drinks less often than others however is probably going to take part in binge drinking when they do. Individuals from this gathering are 2.5 occasions bound to be male than female.

Functional Subtype

The Functional subtype is your opinion about when you hear "functional alcoholics." Making up 19.5% of alcoholics, this is the gathering that is holding down positions and connections. This gathering will in general be moderately aged (around 41). Individuals from this gathering for the most part begin drinking later (around 18) and create liquor reliance later (around 37). This gathering experience moderate paces of depression however lower paces of most other co-happening issues. Numerous individuals from this gathering smoke cigarettes, however few have other substance use issues. Around 60% of this gathering are male.

Of all subtypes, the functional subtype is the to the least extent liable to have lawful issues, and they are the most drastically averse to report issues because of their drinking. They have the most noteworthy education levels and pay of a wide range of alcoholics. A big part of this gathering are hitched. These are individuals that may appear to have their coexistences, the ones that others gaze upward to. Be that it may, while they are "functional" it might be said, they are as yet experiencing compulsion.

Intermediate Familial Subtype

The intermediate familial subtype represents 18.8% of alcoholics. This gathering will, in general, beginning drinking younger (around 17) and builds up a liquor reliance prior (around 32). This subgroup is probably going to have had close family individuals with alcoholism. They also have a high likelihood of experiencing an enemy of social character problems, depression, summed up uneasiness, and bipolar issues. This gathering additionally experiences high paces of cigarette, marijuana, and cocaine compulsion.

The intermediate familial subtype is 64% male. This gathering has an advanced education level than most, yet not as high as the practical subtype. More individuals from this gathering have everyday positions than some others. However, their pay level will, in general, be lower than the utilitarian subtype. While this gathering isn't particularly prone to look for treatment, those that do will, in general, go-to self-improvement gatherings, strength treatment programs, detoxification projects, and private medical care suppliers.

Young Antisocial Subtype

21.1% of alcoholics fall into the youthful antisocial subtype. In general, this gathering will begin drinking at the youngest age (around 15) and builds up a liquor dependence at the most punctual age (around 18). Over half of this gathering have characteristics of against social character issue. They also have high paces of depression, bipolar confusion, social fear, and the top urgent problem. Likewise, this gathering has the most elevated paces of other substance misuse problems, including dependence on cigarettes, weed, meth, cocaine, and narcotics. More than 3/4 of the individuals from this gathering are male. This gathering has the most minimal degrees of education, work, and pay of any gathering. This gathering likewise drinks more at one time and more generally speaking than another gathering, even though they drink marginally less oftentimes. Then again, this gathering is bound to look for help than practically some other, with 35% having searched out some help with defeating alcoholism. This gathering has the most noteworthy pace of looking for treatment from a private medical care supplier, yet additionally frequently picks self-improvement gatherings, strength therapy projects, and detox programs.

Chronic Severe Subtype

The persistent extreme subtype makes up the littlest level of alcoholics, with just 9.2%. This gathering will, in general, beginning drinking at a youthful age (around 15); however, it commonly builds up an alcohol dependence at a moderate age (around 29). 77% of this gathering have close family individuals with alcoholism, the most elevated level of any subtype. 47% of the individuals from this gathering display hostility to social character issues, the second most elevated pace of any subtype. This subtype is the most probable of any to encounter significant depression, dysthymia, bipolar turmoil, summed up nervousness problem, social fear, and frenzy issue Likewise is this gathering e, is probably going to encounter dependence on cigarettes, marijuana, cocaine, and narcotics. Over 80% of these gathering encounters intense alcohol withdrawal and persevering endeavors to chop down. Over 90% experience drinking despite the issues it causes them and drinking bigger sums and for more than planned. This gathering, likewise, will, in general, invest critical measures of energy recuperating from alcohol, and many experiences decreased exercises because of drinking. This gathering additionally sees the most elevated pace of trauma center visits because of drinking. This gathering has the most elevated paces of separation and partition.

Causes of Alcoholism

Alcohol use disorder (AUD) can come from various components. After an extensive stretch of drinking, your mind starts to depend on alcohol to deliver certain synthetic compounds. This is the thing that makes it hard for hefty drinkers to stop and can cause awkward withdrawal indications.

Here's a breakdown of how each one performs a function within the development of alcohol abuse.

Alcohol use disorder (AUD) can come from different factors. After an extensive stretch of ingesting, your cerebrum begins to depend upon alcohol to deliver certain chemicals. This is the thing that makes it hard for alcoholic give up and can cause uncomfortable withdrawal signs and symptoms. Numerous of the maximum not unusual reasons of alcoholism are:

- Biological factors
- Environmental factors
- Social factors
- Psychological factors

Here's a breakdown of how everyone assumes a part in the development of alcohol abuse.

Biological Factors

Research has shown a nearby connection between alcoholism and biological factors, especially genetics and physiology. While a few people can restrict the measure of alcohol they devour, others feel a strong impulse to continue onward. For a few, alcohol radiates feelings of pleasure, encouraging the brain to rehash the conduct. Dreary conduct like this can make you more vulnerable to developing alcoholism. There are likewise sure chemicals in the brain that can make you more helpless to alcohol abuse. For example, scientists have demonstrated that alcohol dependence might be related to up to 51 genes in different chromosome regions. In the event that these genes are gone down through generations, relatives are significantly more inclined to developing drinking problems.

Environmental Factors

As of late, studies have investigated a potential association between your environment and the danger of AUD. For example, numerous researchers have analyzed whether an individual's nearness to alcohol retail locations or bars affects their odds of alcoholism. Individuals who live nearer to alcohol establishments are said to have a more uplifting point of view toward drinking and are bound to take an interest in the action. Moreover, alcohol manufacturers are assaulting the overall population with advertisements. A significant number of these advertisements show drinking as a satisfactory, fun, and loosening up diversion. In only forty years – somewhere in the range of 1971 and 2011 alcohol promotion in the US expanded by in excess of 400 percent.

Another environmental factor, pay, can likewise assume a part in the measure of alcohol an individual consumes. In opposition to prevalent thinking, people who come from wealthy areas are bound to drink than those living beneath neediness. Gallup's new yearly utilization propensities survey showed that about 78 percent of individuals with a yearly family pay of $75,000 or more consume alcohol. This is fundamentally higher than the 45 percent of individuals who drink alcohol and have a yearly family pay of under $30,000.

Social Factors

Social factors can add to an individual's perspectives on drinking. Your culture, religion, family, and work impact large numbers of your behaviors, including drinking. Family assumes the greatest part in an individual's probability of developing alcoholism. Kids who are presented to alcohol abuse since the beginning are more in danger of falling into a dangerous drinking pattern.

Psychological Factors

Diverse psychological factors may build the odds of heavy drinking. Each individual handle circumstance in their own interesting manner. Nonetheless, what you adapt to these sentiments can mean for certain behavioral traits. For instance, individuals with high stress, anxiety, depression, and other mental health conditions are more defenseless against developing alcoholism. In these sorts of conditions, alcohol is regularly used to stifle sentiments and ease the symptoms of psychological disorders.

Alcoholism Risk Factors

There are many risk factors engaged with the potential for developing alcoholism. Alcoholism risk factors don't mean you will develop a drinking issue; in any case, they should fill in as a prevention measure. In the party that you have at least one risk factor, talk with a medical health professional about alcoholism warning signs and prevention assets. A few basic alcohol misuse risk factors are the following:

Drinking at an Early Age

Drinking with alcohol at a young age can prompt issues later on throughout everyday life, particularly in your 20s and 30s. This is particularly obvious when adolescents engage in incessant binge drinking. While drinking from the beginning can increase the probability of alcohol abuse, alcoholism can influence anybody at any age.

Family History with Alcohol Addiction

Growing up around relatives and close family members that experience the ill effects of heavy alcohol increases the risk of alcohol abuse for the next generations to come. At the point when you're encircled by individuals who drink unnecessarily, you can see alcohol use contrastingly and succumb to unfortunate propensities.

High Levels of Stress

Drinking with an end goal to lessen stress can rapidly turn tricky. Career ways that are bound to confront significant degrees of stress because of extended periods and strenuous undertakings incorporate doctors, nurses, emergency rescue workers, construction workers, and the military. It's significant for experts of any industry to discover alternative approaches to destress to forestall alcohol abuse.

Peer Pressure

At the point when a partner or dear companion every now and again drinks, you might be more disposed to go along with them. Surrendering to peer pressure can prompt drinking issues as it were, just as numerous unexpected issues that emerge from over-the-top alcohol utilization. As opposed to wanting to drink, offer to be a designated driver.

Frequent Alcohol Consumption Over a Long Period

When drinking an excessive amount of turns into an example, you significantly increase your odds of building up an alcohol-related issue. The more you drink, the more your body fabricates a resistance to alcohol. Resilience implies you'll require more alcohol to feel similar affects you used to feel with less.

Mixing Alcohol with Other Drugs

Drinking alcohol to intensify or descend off the high of different drugs, for example, prescription opioids, benzodiazepines, or cocaine is a type of polysubstance abuse and can increase the danger of building up a genuine alcohol issue.

Mixing alcohol with different drugs – including those recommended by a specialist – can prompt genuine wellbeing outcomes without taking appropriate consideration. For example, mixing alcohol with opioids, or even drugs for depression or anxiety can prompt negative side effects, for example, increased sedation, respiratory depression, and memory blackouts with large doses.

Binge Drinking

Binge drinking, which includes drinking an exorbitant measure of alcohol inside a short window of time, can likewise be a risk factor for alcoholism. For well-endowed individuals, this implies drinking at least five drinks in a setting, and at least four for ladies.

This degree of drinking is generally regular among young adults between the ages of 18 and 34. It's no fortuitous event that numerous individuals at this age are going to college and bound to get immersed in "party culture".

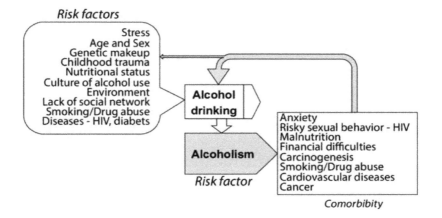

The Disease of Addiction

While there are numerous reasons that an individual may start to drink, individuals with the disease of alcoholism will locate those underlying reasons presently don't drive their drinking designs. At Starting points, we accept that alcoholism is a sickness that impacts the psyche, body, and spirit.

The Physical Allergy

At the point when the disease of alcoholism has grabbed hold, the alcoholic will start to drink more than they expect. Typical drinkers (people without alcoholism) will find that they are effectively ready to restrict the number of drinks that they burn-through. For the alcoholic, this may appear to be outlandish. They start to "lose all control of their liquor consumption once they start to drink." For them, the main drink sets off a hankering for more alcohol which can prompt a binge or gorge. This can bring about consequences that the individual might not have in any case experienced on the off danger that that they had the option to stop after the first drink.

The Mental Obsession

Even after an alcoholic has gone through medical detox and alcohol is not, at this point gift inside the frame, the disease of alcoholism is as yet grinding away. This is maybe the most wicked segment of the disease as it is hard to understand, in any event, for the alcoholic. Alcoholics who are caught in the pattern of fixation keep on getting back to the very substance that is obliterating their life. They may do this regardless of a staggering longing to stop drinking once and for all. For those confronting the sickness, determination alone isn't sufficient to remain sober. They become engrossed with the conviction that they can "control and enjoy" their drinking. Those of us in recuperation allude to this unusual mental bend as the "mental obsession."

It's an obsession to drink normally. An obsession to drink without consequences. An obsession to limit its destruction. An obsession to drink in secret wanting to trick the family, companions, and businesses who know precisely what the issue is.

Why People Relapse?

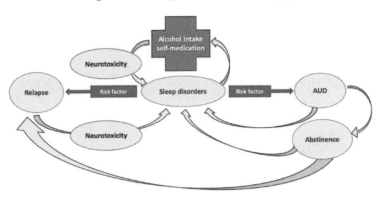

Remaining healthy and keeping up your sobriety requires significant investment and dedication. Shockingly, a few people relapse after alcohol treatment. Triggers, including a gathering of companions who drink, certain exercises or conditions can lead somebody to fall once again into old drinking habits.

Relapsing doesn't mean you've fizzled and can't beat alcoholism. It makes you mindful of triggers and may rouse you to look for extra assistance from a guide or care group. Participating in on-going treatment strategies furnishes you with a more prominent possibility for long-term sobriety than the individuals who don't proceed with recuperation with maintenance programs.

Reasons why some people relapse are:

- Old habits
- Stress and anxiety
- Social pressures

- Mental or emotional instability

- Anger or frustration

- Temptation to feel drunk again

Treatment is the initial move toward a superior tomorrow. Alcohol treatment experts work with you to make a customized far reaching recuperation plan with quantifiable objectives. Thorough recuperation plans may incorporate inpatient or outpatient treatment, prescription helped treatment, directing, and uphold gatherings.

9+1 Way to Quit drinking

1. Work out a plan

Regardless of whether you're meaning to drink less or to stop through and through, it's a smart thought to have an arrangement. A few people like to stop in one go. Others like to gradually decrease their drinking. Everybody is unique so work out what turns out best for you. Recollect that your primary care physician can help you in case you don't know. Your arrangement may be just about as straightforward as drinking one less glass each time you go out. In the event that you need to be more definite, have a consider your:

- Goals — why do you want to lessen or quit drinking?
- Triggers — why and when do you drink?
- Strategies — how will you reduce or quit alcohol?
- Support — who will you turn to for help?

Your goals

Having an unmistakable objective as a main priority can assist you with remaining inspired. Individuals lessen or stop alcohol for some, reasons, including to be better, to set aside cash, or to have more energy.

Your triggers

In case you don't know what your triggers are, it very well may be difficult to drink less. To work out why you're drinking alcohol, ask yourself the following questions:

- where are the spots, I drink the most?
- what times do I drink the most?
- would I like to drink or do I feel compelled?

When you know why you drink, you can work out approaches to stay away from circumstances where you may be enticed to drink.

Your strategies

Have a few systems set up so you're readied when you're enticed by alcohol. You'll realize what to do on the off chance that you surprisingly end up at an occasion where alcohol is being served.

It's a smart thought to keep away from your triggers to assist you with stopping or diminish alcohol. On the off chance that alcohol highlights in your public activity, you could:

- put together without alcohol occasions with your companions as opposed to going out for a beverage
- recommend settings where mocktails are accessible
- get up to speed over an espresso rather than at the bar

· mingle all the more frequently with companions who don't drink

Inside the event that you can't keep a strategic distance from your triggers, try to alternate the alcohol for something one of a kind. for example, on the off danger that you drink prior to going out to feel less on edge, get together with an old buddy all things considered.

Your support

In the same way as other things throughout everyday life, stopping or diminishing alcohol is a lot simpler with help. Educate your loved ones concerning what you're doing so they can help you. It's stunningly better on the off chance that you know somebody who is attempting to do something very similar. You can uphold one another.

2. Talk about it

Letting others realize approximately your desire to stop consuming may additionally help encourage you to stick with your choice.

Involve your loved ones

Loved ones can give consolation and backing when you quit ingesting. by way of opening up about your relationship with alcohol, you may likewise urge others to investigate their own drinking propensities. Possibly your partner, sibling, or roommate is likewise considering rolling out an improvement. Changing drinking propensities together permits you to help one another while additionally boosting your inspiration and responsibility. The person should take notes of the significance of bringing along a confided in help individual when going to occasions that include alcohol. It's frequently simpler to turn down a drink when you don't need to do it single-handedly.

ind a community

constructing new relationships with folks who additionally pick to avoid alcohol may have a whole lot of gain.

"The more help you've got, the better"

Here are some ideas:

- Rather than testing your determination by joining your co-workers for the standard party time, why not welcome an alternate co-specialist to look at the new bakery down the road?
- Consider developing friendship and romance with individuals who don't focus on drinking as a significant piece of their life.
- Miss the bar atmosphere? Contingent upon where you reside, you could possibly visit a sober bar and socialize without alcohol.
- test out apps like Meetup to find other humans interested in alcohol free activities.

Know what to say

whilst you turn down a drink, humans may ask why. you're now not obligated to provide info, however it may help to have a move-to reaction ready:

- "I am cutting back for my fitness."
- "I do not like the way consuming makes me experience."

All things considered, you don't have to say anything over "No, thanks." Practicing your refusal early can help you feel better and sure when you end up in a circumstance that includes alcohol. Make an effort not to stress over others judging you since the vast majority likely will not notice or recollect what you do. at the off chance that you want to offer friends and family a more nitty-gritty clarification however feels uncertain about what to say, it assists with keeping your clarification straightforward:

- "i have been ingesting plenty without a clear cause, and I want to spend some time rethinking that dependency."
- "I catch myself ingesting once I do not want to stand my feelings, and that I want to get higher at working thru them without alcohol."
- "I do not simply enjoy ingesting, and i am bored with doing it simply due to the fact anyone else does."

3. Change your environment

At the point when alcohol makes up a piece of your average everyday practice, drinking can become something of an automatic reaction, particularly when you feel overpowered. You should not have to totally rethink your life to stop drinking, yet a couple of changes in your surroundings can have a major effect.

Get rid of your alcohol

Alcohol in your home can tempt you when you're attempting to quit. on the off risk that you are feeling like a drink, realizing you'll need to go out and create a purchase can discourage you adequately long to locate a decent distraction. Save non-alcoholic drinks close by for yourself as well as other people. You don't have to bring to the table alcohol to be a decent host. Allow guests to bring their own alcohol — and take it with them when they leave. In the event that you live with roommates, consider requesting that they keep their alcohol far out rather than in shared open spaces.

Find a new favorite drink

Picking the correct substitution refreshment can help you stand firm in your craving to quit drinking. Plain water may offer a lot of health benefits, however, it's truly not the most intriguing decision. With a little imagination, you can discover something enjoyable that doesn't make you miss your favorite drink. Try:

- injecting plain or shining water with cleaved natural products or spices
- adding cinnamon sticks or flavors to tea, apple juice, or hot cocoa
- blending juice or lemonade in with shining water

Vary your routine

At the point when you will in general drink at a specific season of day, accomplishing something different is probably the most ideal approaches to break that design. Exercises that get you out of the house and moving regularly help most. Consider the following ideas:

- On the off chance that you typically meet companions for a drink after work, consider taking a walk or meeting them for a home base in the recreation center or other sans alcohol space.

- Rather than going to your typical eatery for supper and drinks, why not attempt another spot that doesn't serve alcohol? You'll will encounter something strange without feeling enticed to drink.

- Start cooking at home to occupy yourself and set aside some cash.

At the point when your craving to drink adjusts more to your temperament than a specific season of day, having a couple of elective adapting techniques prepared can help:

- Instead of taking a drink to calm anxiety, try <u>affirmations</u>, <u>deep breathing</u>, or <u>meditation</u>.

- Comfort yourself when feeling <u>lonely</u> by reaching out to a loved one or watching a favorite movie.

4. Make time for self-care

Stopping drinking can feel pretty upsetting. In the event that you go to alcohol to oversee passionate distress, the additional overpower can incite the inclination to drink, causing accomplishment to appear to be considerably more unattainable. It's not unexpected to battle when rolling out huge improvements, yet great self-care practices can assist you with overseeing overpowering emotions and deal with your brain and body.

Prioritize wellness

Feeling at your best physically can support versatility and enthusiastic strength, preparing you to climate moves that trigger the longing to drink. By avoiding alcohol, you're stepping toward improving physical wellbeing. As you notice those medical advantages, you'll probably feel more invigorated and motivatedto keep up your advancement.

Different tips to consider:

- Stay hydrated.

- Eat ordinary, adjusted suppers. Attempt to incorporate nourishments that increment energy and lift temperament.

- Get ordinary active work, in case you're capable. Take a stab at climbing, cycling, moving, or roller-skating for charming approaches to remain dynamic.

- Focus on better rest. A decent objective for most grown-ups is 7 to 9 hours.

Rediscover hobbies

Numerous individuals use alcohol to adapt to weariness. Fulfilling leisure activities can divert you from wanting to drink, however, they likewise help you relax —something everybody needs to do. In case you've lately wound-up aching to get once more into an old hobby, presents an ideal opportunity to put it all on the line. Technology makes it simpler than at any other time to master new abilities and find innovative methods of interfacing, in any event, when you can't truly partake in exercises with others.

You also might try:

- Do-It-Yourself home activities
- building or painting models
- board or computer games
- chipping in
- sitting back with a decent book

Keep Record

Possibly you've never had any interest in logging your deepest thoughts, however journaling can be an incredible instrument to follow your emotions as you work on quitting alcohol. Investigating, recorded as a hard copy, what you find troublesome and when you most need to drink can help you notice designs that offer more understanding into your alcohol use. Contrasting the emotions that surface when you have a drink with the sentiments you experience while declining likewise causes you to perceive when drinking doesn't fix the issues you're attempting to oversee. A journal likewise offers a helpful space to list reasons you need to quit and brainstorm exercises to supplant drinking.

Explore new tools to cope

When you distinguish a portion of the primary reasons why you drink, you can start finding new techniques for tending to those triggers.

The most supportive way of dealing with stress frequently relies upon the conditions:

- At the point when you feel pitiful however need alone time, you should seriously think about a most loved collection or soothing book.
- At the point when you need to drink to evade relationship struggle or stress, you may vent to a family member or friend or practice better relational abilities to reconnect with your accomplice.
- On the off chance that forlornness triggers the craving to drink, you may investigate approaches to associate with removed companions or investigate approaches to fabricate new fellowships.

5. Reach out for support

Quitting alcohol all alone is harder for some than others, yet there's no compelling reason to go it single-handedly. In case you're struggling to adhere to your objective or simply need some additional guidance, consider connecting for proficient support. On the off chance that you feel good doing as such, raise your difficulties to your essential healthcare supplier. Finding a therapist can likewise be an extraordinary beginning stage on the off chance that you're not open to opening up to your healthcare supplier. It may likewise merit looking at a 12-venture program in your general vicinity, similar to Alcoholics Mysterious or Shrewd Recuperation, to check whether it seems like something that may be useful for you.

6. Drinking non-alcoholic drinks

In the realm of non-drinkers non-alcoholic beers, wines and spirits are Extremely questionable. Many contend they ought to be completely evaded as they are risky triggers, and just help individuals to remember what they're missing, consequently hauling them onto that tricky slant. However, for some others, myself notwithstanding, they're a lifeline. On the off chance that an individual went through a few evenings in pubs drinking non-alcoholic beers and nobody has ever seen so he would be off the booze – handy if you need to dodge any abnormal inquiries, or can't be tried to guard your choice not to feel unpleasant the following day. It unquestionably feels like there's some sort of psychologically relieving impact of airing out that booze-free brew or popping that 'Nosecco' cork. We realized as of late that it takes alcohol seven minutes to hit the brain, so maybe it's not very unlike that fake introductory 'relief' you get when drinking the genuine article. Within the online groups we follow there have been numerous discussions about which ones are the awesome, are the ones that are most normally suggested by individuals aware of everything – alongside a couple of my favorites.

Note that most some are 0.5%. However, this is so low it's, in fact, viewed as AF (sans alcohol):

- BrewDog Babysitter State (0.5%) – broadly considered to the best non-alcoholic lager
- Nosecco (0.5%) – Numerous individuals like this, yet it tastes rather sweet.
- Crodino (0.0%)– We found this while on vacation in Italy. This non-alcoholic aperitif is an ideal option in contrast to a boozy Aperol Spritz!olic.

7. Make the most out of your hangover-free mornings

Perhaps the best thing about surrendering alcohol – close by better sleep, weight loss, clearer skin, and having more cash – is restoring the time you would've spent hungover on the couch. Presently you should've recovered your ends of the week, you ought to choose to benefit as much as possible from your recently discovered time and energy by running. we know it's not for everybody, but rather we'd recommend attempting to discover something you love that you had neither the time nor the energy for in the wake of drinking. It very well may be heating, doing a wellness DVD, or basically orchestrating all the earlier morning excursions with the children.

An individual began two or three years back however halted when his hangovers began enduring a few days. In those days, he was unable to run for over two minutes without needing a break – that is no distortion – yet, he slowly moved gradually up to 5k with the Couch to 5k digital recording. This is a splendid and FREE webcast of guided runs that progressively develop until before you know it you can run for 30 minutes ceaselessly. Indeed, even the super-incredulous author Charlie Brooker is a fan.

He proceeded onward from 5K and downloaded a running application by Verv. Alongside the 5K, it additionally incorporates other steady exercises to help you arrive at 10K, a half long-distance race, or a full long-distance race. In addition to the side of this one is you can pick between a lot of various soundtracks and it additionally tracks your distance, speed, GPS course, and calories consumed.

8. Build up your motivation to change

At the point when we directed our drinking from the outset, we monitored how we felt in the wake of drinking, so we could help ourselves to remember those negative effects before we began drinking. When we quit, we observed how much better we felt, making a point to see how composed we felt and how we felt a great deal more profitable in the mornings. From the outset, we didn't know we needed to stop by any means. Presently, we realize we'll never drink again, and we're so cheerful we did it. Over the long haul, our inspiration developed further instead of more fragile

9. Using Natural remedies to quit drinking

Albeit a basic glass of wine is useful for your cardiovascular wellbeing, in the event that you wind up gorging on in excess of a couple, you are putting your psychological and actual wellbeing at high danger. Indeed, an examination distributed in the diary Australian Therapist expresses that unreasonable drinking may prompt drunkorexia in young ladies. This is a harming and perilous practice where individuals miss dinners to repay the calorie consumption because of alcohol. Dieticians and specialists exhort carefully against this way of life because of its undeniable risks. You will positively experience the ill effects of different inadequacies as alcohol contains for all intents and purposes no wholesome substance other than void calories

- **Grapes:**

Quite possibly the most mainstream and normal approaches to control alcohol compulsion is having grapes. At whatever point you pine for a drink of alcohol, simply have a glass of grape squeeze or eat a lot of grapes all things being equal. Since they are the source from which wine is made, grapes fill in as an extraordinary option for weighty drinkers. Additionally, these natural products are wealthy in potassium, which causes your body to keep a basic blood balance, alongside invigorating the kidneys. Grapes can likewise purify poisons from the liver successfully.

- **Fruit Juices**

This common cure is something that works for some individuals. In the event that you are a solid alcoholic, you need to incorporate new, custom made juices in your eating regimen to dispose of your alcohol habit. These juices are loaded up with nutrient A, folate, nutrient C, calcium, magnesium, and potassium and can go about as an option at whatever point you want to have a drink.

- **Date Juice**

If you are engaging to adapt to alcohol enslavement, at that point have dates consistently. These organic products have certain properties which help in detoxifying and getting out poisons from your liver. Absorb a few dates water for one hour and later eliminate the seeds and crush them in the water. Have this drink two times each day for a very long time to accomplish the ideal outcomes.

- **Bitter Gourd Juice**

Severe gourd recuperates liver harm because of abundance alcohol utilization. This vegetable is a characteristic remedy that flushes out poisons from your body. To make the drink, separate juice from a couple of severe gourd leaves and blend 3 tsp in a glass of buttermilk. Have the blend on an unfilled stomach consistently for a couple of months to dispose of alcohol enslavement.

- **Carrot Juice**

Carrot is likewise one of the go-to fixings with regards to controlling the inclinations of drinking alcohol. This is because carrots have numerous medical advantages and supplements just as nutrients. At whatever point you want to drink alcohol, simply have a glass of carrot juice. This will cause you to feel better as it improves processing and treats alcohol fixation. Have a glass of carrot squeeze day by day to dispose of your alcohol longings.

10.   Don't Give Up

No place in this article did we say it is not difficult to quit drinking! Remember your objectives alongside the reasons you even set these objectives in any case. In the event that you have an lots of drinks one evening, don't allow it to ruin the objective you're going after. Simply get directly in the groove again the following day. At the point when you bomb yourself, simply recollect this statement by Robert F. Kennedy: "Just the individuals who try to flop extraordinarily can at any point accomplish significantly." You will succeed on the off chance that you really need to get your drinking propensities leveled out or quit drinking by and large.

Suppose that you have an objective to diminish your drinking, say it so anyone can hear like your companions or family, or even record it. Making a responsibility for all to hear or on paper implies you're substantially more liable to adhere to your objectives. Telling your loved ones can likewise help you feel more upheld as you make changes, and as you gain ground.

Conclusion

Alcohol is anything but a normal item. While it conveys undertones of joy and amiability in the personalities of many, hurtful results of its use are assorted and boundless

From a worldwide viewpoint, to decrease the mischief caused by alcohol, arrangements need to consider explicit circumstances in various social orders. Normal volumes burned-through and examples of drinking are two components of alcohol utilization that should be considered in endeavors to lessen the weight of alcohol-related issues. Keeping away from the mix of drinking and driving is an illustration of measures that can decrease the wellbeing weight of alcohol.

Public checking frameworks should be created to monitor alcohol utilization and its results and to bring issues to light among people in general and strategy producers. It is up to the two governments and concerned residents to empower discuss and plan powerful general wellbeing approaches that limit the mischief caused by alcohol.

The vast majority believe they're halting drinking since they're exhausted from feeling hangover. Or then again, they need to be better or set aside cash. On the whole, those are also great purposes behind stopping, yet they're likely not the simple explanation you're doing this. You're genuine 'why" goes a lot further than that – and this is actually what you need to tap into. To prevail with regards to lessening your drinking, you likewise need to break affiliations. For instance, in the event that you will, in general, reach for a drink when you get back home from work, plan an elective action to attempt to break this connection. It is essential to empower yourself en route.

Regardless of whether your advancement has been little, give yourself some acclaim. Consider how you can remunerate yourself for the advancement you've made. For instance, on the off chance that you've set aside cash, could you treat yourself to something that you will appreciate, similar to a takeaway or some new garments? The best rewards are close to home to you and prompt.

Quit Drinking for Women

A 28-Day Alcohol-Free Challenge to Eradicate Your Worst Habit
and Get Your Life Back on Track

Allison Alcantara

Contents

Prologue 146

    What you should know about Alcohol 148

    What are the different drinking levels? 148

    When is moderate drinking still too much? 149

    How Long Does Alcohol Stay In The Body? 150

    What is a standard drink? 151

    How do you know how much alcohol is in your drink? 151

    Women and Alcohol 152

WEEK ONE 156

    Day ONE 157

    Day TWO 163

    Day THREE 166

    Day FOUR 169

    Day FIVE 172

    Day Six 174

    Day Seven 178

WEEK TWO 180

    DAY EIGHT AND NINE 182

    Day Ten and Eleven 185

Day Twelve and Thirteen 187

Day Fourteen... 189

WEEK THREE 193

DAY FIFTEEN TO TWENTY-ONE 196

WEEK FOUR 200

DAY TWENTY-TWO TO TWENTY-FOUR........................ 206

DAY TWENTY-FIVE AND TWENTY-SIX 211

DAY TWENTY-SEVEN AND TWENTY-EIGHT 216

Epilogue.. 219

Prologue

Quitting alcohol is one of the biggest challenges people face. It starts with not knowing you have a drinking problem to accepting it, then gradually working on it while avoiding temptations and situations that put you in that place at the first time along comes staying sober, and finally managing your urges.

One other problem people trying to quit faces is depression. Because alcohol has been their go-to when they are sad or when they want to unwind and take a moment from certain responsibilities, it becomes a challenge and that is when looking for an alternative comes in.

For some people, it is very easy looking for an alternative, either an activity or a non-alcoholic substitute while for others nothing seem to just work. With adequate motivation and zeal, everyone can successfully quit a bad habit.

According to experts, it takes 21 days to quit a habit and they attribute the "21 days to break a habit" myth to Dr Maxwell Maltz, who worked as a plastic surgeon before becoming a psychologist.

In his work, he suggested that it would take about 3 weeks to get used to:

- different facial features after plastic surgery
- the absence of a limb after amputation
- a house they've just moved into

The authenticity of this claim can be questioned as Dr Maltz seemed to rely only on the reports of patients instead of hard scientific evidence. Some persons believe there is a truth in this claim.

In today's world, it has been shown that alcohol use in women increases with each year and the negative effects are far more deleterious in the female gender than their male counterparts. In this book, we will work through a story case study that will help us with practical exercises geared towards enabling you to quit drinking.

"Marie who was born to a not so affluent home grew up becoming very smart lady bagging all the awards from her secondary school days through her University years. She worked hard and had a passion for the Real Estate Industry and not long after she graduated from the University, a top real estate company offered her a good job. This not only provided her with enough money to take care of her family, but it also expanded

her social horizon and by default her lifestyle — attending dinners and Galas and unwinding after work with her colleagues in bars — this spurred new habits. She didn't even notice how these relationships ate deep into her moral fabric. It was safe to say she was a wrecking ball and would soon destroy her standards".

In the next couple of days. We would attempt mechanisms and guides to quit drinking.

What you should know about Alcohol

Alcohol is a psychoactive drug and it is the active ingredient in beer, wine, and spirits. Its recreational activity can be due to the effect on the brain as it causes the release of dopamine — the rewarding hormone —.

Alcoholism which is also known as Alcohol use disorder or excessive alcohol use is a bad drinking habit. It is a medical condition in which a person develops the urge to drink alcohol despite the negative impacts it poses on their lives. The National Institute on Alcohol Abuse and Alcoholism (NIAAA) describes alcohol use disorder as "problem drinking that becomes severe."

What are the different drinking levels?

According to the 2015-2020, Dietary Guidelines for American, moderate drinking can be defined as drinking up to 1 drink per day for women of legal drinking age and up to 2 drinks per day for men of legal drinking age.

When is moderate drinking still too much?

It is safest to avoid alcohol altogether if you are:

- Taking medications that interact with alcohol
- Managing a medical condition that can be made worse by drinking
- Underage
- Planning to drive a vehicle or operate machinery
- Participating in activities that require skill, coordination, and alertness
- Recovering from alcohol use disorder or unable to control the amount they drink
- Pregnant or trying to become pregnant

Excessive alcohol use includes but is not limited to:

- **Binge Drinking**: The term is used to define the heavy consumption of alcohol over a long period. In the United States, the consumption of four or more drinks in a row by women at least once in the previous two weeks can be seen as binge drinking, and the term heavy binge drinking includes three or more such episodes in 2 weeks. Several studies have shown that people who binge drink heavily may have some symptoms of alcoholism.

- **Heavy Drinking**: the National Institute on Alcohol Abuse and Alcoholism (NIAAA) defines heavy alcohol use as more than 3 drinks on a day for a woman while the Substance Abuse and Mental Health Services Administration (SAMHSA) defines heavy alcohol use as binge drinking on 5 or more days in the past month.
- Any drinking by pregnant women or those under 21

How Long Does Alcohol Stay In The Body?

The mechanism by which alcohol is removed from the body system follows a zero-order kinetic, which means to say independent of the concentration of the alcohol in the system the rate at which it is eliminated from the body is fixed. This is different from the rate of elimination of some other regular drugs where an increase in concentration will also increase the rate at which it leaves the body.

It is on this basis that intoxication occurs. For example; a person that drinks one bottle of 40 per cent alcohol and another that drinks one bottle of 15 per cent alcohol will still eliminate the alcohol within the same duration. With a higher concentration, the risk of increased side effects and toxicity is certain. On average, it takes about 6 hours for a standard drink to be metabolized from the body.

What is a standard drink?

Knowing what counts as a standard drink will help you know the limit of alcohol safe to consume. Many people are surprised to learn what counts as a drink. The amount of liquid in your glass, can, or bottle does not necessarily match up to how much alcohol is actually in your drink. Different types of beer, wine, or malt liquor can have very different amounts of alcohol content. For example, many light beers have almost as much alcohol as regular beer – about 85% as much. Here's another way to put it:

- Regular beer: 5% alcohol content
- Some light beers: 4.2% alcohol content

How do you know how much alcohol is in your drink?

It is important to know how much alcohol your drink contains. In the United States, one "standard" drink (or one alcoholic drink equivalent) contains roughly 14 grams of pure alcohol, which is found in 12 ounces of regular beer, which is usually about 5% alcohol, 5 ounces of wine, which is typically about 12% alcohol, 1.5 ounces of distilled spirits, which is about 40% alcohol.

Even though they come in different sizes, the drinks below are each example of one standard drink.

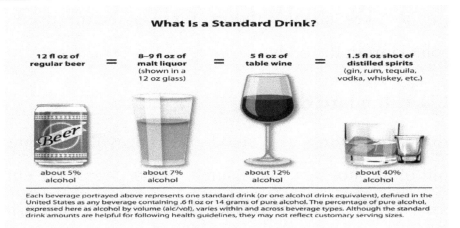

* *The above image was extracted from the NIAAA website*

Below is a table with the definition of a standard drink based on different countries.

One Standard Drink by Country
(grams and milliliters of alcohol)

Country	grams	milliliters
Australia	10 g	13 mL
Canada	13.6 g	17 mL
Ireland	10 g	13 mL
New Zealand	10 g	13 mL
UK	8 g	10 mL
USA	14 g	18 mL

©Nutrientsreview.com

Women and Alcohol

A survey done on the 21 of August 2019 among young youths in the US showed that about 32% of female high school students consumed alcohol compared with 26% of male high school students. Binge drinking was also more common among female (15%) than male (13%) high school students. A 2020 report published in the American Journal of Preventive Medicine found that both current alcohol use and binge drinking among pregnant women aged 18–44 years in the United States increased slightly from 2011 to 2018, both for current drinkers (those having at least one drink of any alcoholic beverage in the past 30 days) and Binge drinkers. Alcohol affects women more different than their male counterparts. The reason for this claim can be attributed to body structure and chemistry. The body of a woman contains less amount of water and more fat cells (adipose) as opposed to the male body which has lesser fat cells. Water dilutes alcohol resulting in lower concentrations in the system and fat retains/stores alcohol exposing the organs to higher. concentrations. So for women, the latter is the case as they possess more fat cells. Another reason for this claim is the reduced quantity of the enzymes alcohol dehydrogenase. This enzyme is responsible for the breakdown of alcohol before it gets to the bloodstream. So at any given amount, the blood level of alcohol will be higher in females than in males and so are the negative consequences.

Seeing the figures of alcoholism rise every year coupled with the more deleterious effect it has on the female gender, for the next four weeks we are going to follow a step-by-step guide in quitting this bad drinking habit.

START WITH A DECISION.

WEEK ONE

Day ONE

Not knowing when it is a Problem

"Marie has had a terrible day at work, apparently she wasn't prepared for her big pitch to secure the multimillion naira contract for her company. After elevating to the position of the Assistant Manager at her company, she relaxed and got very complacent. On the day before her big presentation that was expected to close a huge deal, she was out with the girls. She has had a history of a drinking problem although it wasn't diagnosed yet. One too many times she ended up drinking more or longer than she intends and this night was one of those nights.

She was out clubbing with Sophie and Claire and had consumed much more than she had ever consumed. The last time it happened, she had woken up from bed to a total stranger beside her in her house and she had no idea how she got home from the bar. She always promised herself after several recurrences that she would stop, she always ended up feeling depressed after the deed had been done.

On this fateful evening, Marie just wanted to ease off the anxiousness and tension about her "big day" so she opted for going to the karaoke with Claire and Sophie. They got into a game that involved a penalty of drinking booze if you couldn't complete the lyrics of a song. She just wanted to ease the tension and she delved into the game, she kept on losing and consequently drinking. She was surprised at how much she had consumed without flinching. They teased her saying she drank like a fish. It was all fun and games until one of the guys invited her and her friends to a club nearby.

—The next morning—

Marie woke up not knowing where she was but was grateful she still had her sanity. Not knowing where she was and how she got there, she reached out to get her phone and it was dead. She looked at her watch lying in one corner of the room and jumped up when she saw the time. It was 9:30 am and her presentation was for 9:00 am making her 30 minutes behind schedule.

At 11:00 am Marie was at her workplace. She rushed into the conference room that showed all forms of tardiness. She started setting up for her presentation and asides from her tardiness, she was in utter confusion mixing up her slides and sounding very incompetent. The Presentation lasted for a very short 15 minutes and her supervisor had never been more disappointed with a project as she was with Marie's. She was the brightest and youngest staff and he would have placed a bet on her nailing this presentation. But now he wouldn't talk to her, and she was frustrated. He sent her a message later saying he will contact her after a decision has been made.

Marie got back home feeling very depressed and sad, to say the least. Until now she hasn't admitted that she has a drinking disorder. All these wouldn't have happened if she had not taken any drink or partied that night, her friends were at her house. They explained they were also wasted from the alcohol at the game that they didn't notice her leaving. By this time they already aware of her awful presentation. She sat on her couch, still on her work clothe with five empty bottles of alcohol and a half-empty bottle of beer in one hand. Claire attempted to stop her from drinking but she fought back so she dragged the bottle of beer from her".

It only takes a few mild symptoms to signal the beginning of a drinking problem, knowing these disturbing signs, and working on them on time can help prevent a drinking disorder. Carefully look at the exercise below, do you see any familiar symptoms in yourself? If Yes, don't worry this 28 days step by step guide will help reduce your risks.

- *Exercise*

In the past year (tick all that applies), have you:

- o *Had times when you ended up drinking **more, or longer,** than you intended?*

- o *More than once wanted to **cut down or stop** drinking, or tried to, but couldn't?*

- o *More than once gotten into situations while or after drinking that **increased your chances of getting hurt** (such as driving, swimming, using machinery, walking in dangerous areas, or having unsafe sex)?*

- o *Had to drink **much more** than you once did to **get the effect** you want? Or found that your **usual number** of drinks had **much less effect** than before?*

- o *Continued to drink even though it was making you feel **depressed or anxious** or adding to another health problem? Or after having had a **memory blackout?***

- o *Spend a **lot of time** drinking? Or being sick or getting over other after-effects?*

- o *Continued to drink even though it was causing **trouble** with your **family** or **friends?***

- o *Found that drinking- or being sick from drinking- often **interfered with taking care** of your **home or family**? Or caused job troubles? Or **school** problems?*

o   ***Given up*** *or* ***cut back*** *on* ***activities*** *that were important or interesting to you, or gave you pleasure, to drink?*

o   *More than once gotten* ***arrested,*** *been held at a police station, or had other* ***legal problems*** *because of your drinking?*

o   *Found that when the effects of alcohol are wearing off, you had withdrawal symptoms such as trouble sleeping, shakiness, restlessness, nausea, sweating, a racing heart, or a seizure? Or sensed things that were not there (hallucination)?*

*The questions listed above are based on symptoms for alcohol use disorder in the American Psychiatric Association's Diagnostics and Statistical Manual (DSM) of Mental Disorders, Fourth Edition.

The symptoms at the beginning of the list indicate less severity, but as we go down the list, there is likely to be major concerns as she experiences on or more of the symptoms down the list.

Following Marie's story, we can tick five of these symptoms with one or two of the symptoms appearing towards the end of the list raising a cause for concern. Now it's your turn.

Day TWO

Make a list of pros and cons

Recovery for people with a drinking habit as with any other habit is a gradual process. In the early stages, most people are faced with denial. In the case of Marie, it had to take putting her job on the line to realize that she might have a drinking problem. Sometimes even after acceptance, you might find yourself making excuses and dragging your feet. If you find yourself in this position where you are struggling with the decision. Knowing the benefits and the costs of each choice has been proven to help people with their ambivalence about quitting drinking.

Evaluating the Pros and Cons of drinking

In today's exercise, you will be making a table similar to what is below weighing the Pros and Cons of not drinking to the Pros and Cons of drinking but before you start this exercise practice first by making a list of Pros and Cons from the case study "Marie" above. Have fun doing that and see you tomorrow.

Exercise:

Drinking	*Not Drinking*

Is drinking worth the cost?

Pros	*Pros*

- *It helps me forget about my problems.*
- *I have fun when I drink.*
- *It is my way of relaxing after a stressful day.*

- *My relationship would probably improve.*
- *I'd feel better mentally and physically.*
- *I'd have more time and energy for the people and activities I care about.*

Cons

- *It causes problems in my relationship.*
- *I feel depressed anxious and ashamed of myself.*
- *It gets in the way of my*

Cons

- *I'd have to find another way to deal with problems.*
- *I'd lose my drinking buddies*
- *I'd have to face the*

job performance and family responsibilities.

responsibilities I've been ignoring.

Day THREE

To Cut Down Or To Quit

The decision to quit or cut down on your drinking problem will depend on the severity of the problem. If you're an alcoholic — which, by definition, means you aren't able to control your drinking — it's best to try to stop drinking entirely. But if you're not ready to take that step, or if you don't have an alcohol abuse problem but want to cut back for personal or health reasons, the following tips can help:

- Set your drinking goal: There is an entire exercise on setting your goals and following through in the next chapter (Check Day Four).

- Choose a limit for how much you'll drink, but make sure your limit is not more than one drink a day as a woman and try to have some days each week when you won't drink alcohol at all.

- Write your drinking goal down and keep it where you will frequently see it, such as on your phone or taped to your refrigerator. Check Day four.

- Cut down drinking at home: Eliminate or limit the quantity of alcohol you keep at home. It's much easier to avoid drinking if you don't keep temptations around.

- Drink slower: When you drink, sip slowly and take a break of 30 minutes or one hour between drinks. You can also switch to drinking soda, water, or juice but not alcoholic drinks.

- Drinking on an empty stomach is always a bad idea, so make sure you drink on a full stomach.

Practice:

Schedule one or two alcohol-free days each week. Then, try to stop drinking for one week. Get a Journal and make a note in it about how you feel physically and mentally these days — recognizing the benefits may help you to cut down for good.

Day FOUR

Set A Goal

Set goals and prepare for change. Once you've decided to change, the next step is establishing clear drinking goals.

The more specific, realistic, and clear your goals are, the better.

Example #1: My drinking goal

I will stop drinking alcohol. My quit date is _____.

Example #2: My drinking goal

I will stop drinking on weekdays, starting as of _____.

I will limit my Saturday and Sunday drinking to no more than three drinks per day or five drinks per weekend. After three months, I will cut back my weekend drinking even more to a maximum of two drinks per day and three drinks per weekend.

Do you want to stop drinking altogether or just cut back?

If your goal is to reduce your drinking, decide which days you will drink alcohol and how many drinks you will allow yourself per day as shown in the latter part of the examples above. Try to commit to at least two days each week when you won't drink at all.

For those completely cutting done, when do you want to stop drinking or start drinking less? Tomorrow? In a week? Next month? Within six months?

If you're trying to stop drinking, we are set a specific quit date.

Practice:

Set a specific quit date on your journal (it must be easily accessible).

Day FIVE

Accomplish Your Goals

After you've set your goals to cut back on your drinking, write down some ideas on how you can help yourself accomplish these goals.

For example:

Get rid of temptations: Remove all alcohol, barware, and other alcohol-related paraphernalia from your home and office.

Announce your goal: Inform your friends, family members, and co-workers, let them know that you're trying to stop or cut back on drinking. If they drink, ask them to support your recovery by not doing so in front of you.

Be upfront about your new limits: Make it clear that drinking will not be allowed in your home and that you may not be able to attend events where alcohol is being served.

Avoid bad influences: You may end up losing friends and social connections, but not to worry, the right one will come. Once you have set up these limits. Separate yourself from people who don't support your efforts to stop drinking or respect the limits you've set. This may mean giving up certain friends and social connections, but not to worry, you'll get more.

Experience is the best teacher: Reflect on previous attempts to stop or reduce your drinking.

What worked? What didn't? What can you do differently this time to avoid pitfalls?

Day Six

Find alternatives

When giving up something that was once your go-to when sad depressed. It is safe to get something to take the place of it. Searching for an alternative to taking the place of drinking in your life will help you to learn how to stay sober while still having fun in social situations. You will be shocked when you realize that there are many different alternatives to alcohol that people turn to in social gatherings to have the satisfaction that makes them feel as though they are drinking without actually risking their sobriety. Have in mind that even a small amount of alcohol can trigger uncontrollable urges if you are a recovering alcoholic.

These alternatives are meant to help you to feel good and achieve muscle relaxation without exposing you to alcohol capable of causing you an addiction or drinking problem.

Below is an outline of suggested alternatives to alcohol gotten from the website of the National Institute on Alcohol Abuse and Alcoholism (NIAAA). Be sure to practice these tips with a sober buddy, sponsor, or mentor to help you achieve your long-term recovery goals.

Here are some of the best alternatives to alcohol consumption:

Alcohol-free drinks (Non-alcoholic beverages)

Try non-alcoholic beverages/beer instead of risking any amount of alcohol consumption. You will get the taste of beer and have something to hold in your hand in social situations where the people around you are drinking. There are even alcohol-free mixed drinks ("mocktails") that taste the same without the negative effects of alcohol.

Additionally, drinks that are carbonated, sparkling, or have a tang to them, such as kombucha, can make you feel like you are drinking alcohol, even though you are completely sober. And the even bigger, long-term benefit of this is that it is better for your physical and mental health.

However, you should note that alcohol-free beers and mocktails do not help everyone. If you are already in recovery and do not have much sober time, these imitation drinks could hinder rather than help your sobriety.

Take time for yourself…

Try muscle relaxation techniques

So many people turn to alcohol to find that sense of relaxation. However, using alcohol to relax does not get to the root problem of why you are experiencing stress in the first place. Guided meditation, exercise, progressive muscle relaxation, yoga, deep breathing, and massage are all alternatives to the release you might feel when you initially pick up a drink.

Set up friend hangouts in places without alcohol

Sometimes, meeting friends at a bar is just not what's best for your recovery needs. Every so often, suggest an alternative plan to hang out—whether that's going on a hike, park, bowling, seeing a movie, etc., you can still find ways to have fun with your loved ones without

the glaring temptation of alcohol.

Day Seven

Reminder strategies

Breaking a habit may be difficult at the initial stage, that is why it helps to have concrete reminders of why and how you've decided to do it. Some standard options include carrying a change plan (More details in Week two) in your wallet or posting sticky notes at home.

Also, consider these high-tech ideas:

Fill out a change plan (refer to week two), email it to your personal (non-work) account, store it in a private online folder, and review it weekly.

Store your goals, reasons, or strategies in your mobile phone as short text messages or notepad entries that you can retrieve when an urge hits.

Set up an automated mobile phone or email calendar alerts that deliver reminders when you choose, such as a few hours before you usually go out. (Email providers such as Gmail and Yahoo mail have online calendars with alert options.)

Create passwords that are motivating phrases in code, which you'll reinforce each time you log in, such as Poco-a-poco, No pain no glory. etc.

Exercise:

Write down Ten (10) motivational phrases or Puns.

WEEK TWO

All of Marie's life, she always dreamt of being in a position where she could be able to provide decent and affordable housing for the low-income earners. Growing up in a shanty neighbourhood with moribund buildings and waking up each day thanking God the roofs didn't fall on you while you were asleep drove her into studying real estate and management. So you can imagine how disappointed and depressed she was after her horrible presentation that would have secured a contract capable of changing the lives of many.

Marie was so good at her job, her follow up on the project was more than anyone could offer. After much consideration, she was awarded the contract and was still placed on four-month probation where she had to attend compulsory Alcoholics Anonymous AA meetings and submit attendance and progress sheets to her company.

This was enough motivation for her and she religiously attended her meetings.

Before we start this week, let us try to identify our motivation, we will be required to go back to this from time to time so I advise you to write it somewhere that is very accessible.

DAY EIGHT AND NINE

Keep Drinking Track

If you want to cut back or quit your drinking, start by keeping track of *every* drink. Find what works best for you. It can also help if you carry a drinking tracker card in your wallet, make check marks on a kitchen calendar, or enter notes in a mobile phone notepad or personal digital assistant.

Making note of each drink before you drink it may help you slow down when needed.

Below are two different forms (Drink tracking cards) you can print, cut out, and keep with you. Both of them help make you aware of patterns and are a key step in planning for a change. Try one form, or try both to see which is more helpful.

The **4-week tracker card** is a simple calendar form. If you mark down each drink before you have it, this can help you slow down if needed.

GOAL: No more than_____drink(s) on any day and _____per week.

Sun	Mon	Tue	Wed	Thu	Fri	Sat
1	2	3	4	5	6	7

Total=

8	9	10	11	12	13	14

Total=

15	16	17	18	19	20	21

Total=

22	23	24	25	26	27	28

Total=

Date	Situation (People, place, activities) or Triggers (Incidents, feelings)	Type of drink(s)	Amount	Consequences

Alcohol Analyzer card extracted from NIAA: This will help to note people, places that trigger the feelings or urges, the type of drinks offered by the person or in that gathering, the amount and the consequences after consumption which are all useful tools when to prevent recurrences.

Day Ten and Eleven

Count and measure

We have talked about what a standard drink is, knowing the standard drink sizes so you can count your drinks accurately is very useful for individuals who want to cut down on their drinking, So if you skipped the prologue, this is the best time to go back and understand what a standard drink is.

The next step is to measure drinks at home. Away from home, it can be hard to keep track, especially with mixed drinks, and at times, you may be getting more alcohol than you think. With wine, you may need to ask the host or server not to "top off" a partially filled glass.

Kindly turn over to get a list of some drinks and their alcohol content.

Stay Safe and Know your Limit

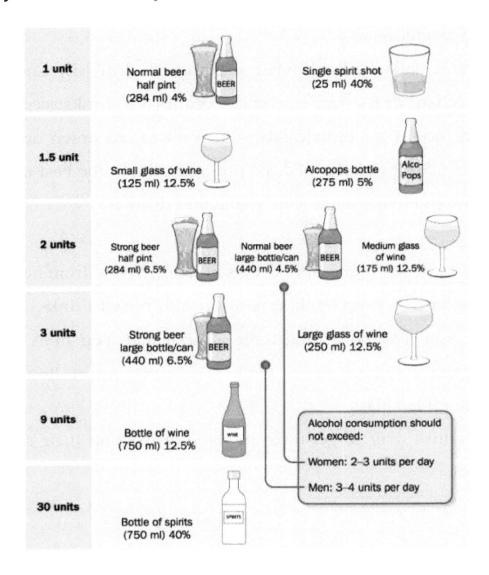

Day Twelve and Thirteen

The change plan

Even when you have committed to making a change, you still may have mixed feelings at times. There are days where a lot of confusion would becloud your mind and it makes you want to grow crazy. To avoid situations such as this Making a written "change plan" this will serve as a reminder strategy that will help you to strengthen your goals, recording reasons why you want to reach them, and how you plan to accomplish them. we have been able to set a goal in the previous week. This week and in the next two days, we will engage in the change plan.

A sample form is provided below. After filling it in, you can print it or email it to yourself to serve as a constant reminder.

THE CHANGE PLAN FORM

Goal: You can also just write down what you set as your goal in the previous week or (select one). This is very critical to continuing and finishing strong in your plans.

- I want to drink no more than ___ drink(s) on any day and no
- more than ___ drink(s) per week (see low-risk drinking limits).
- I want to stop drinking.

Timing: I will start on this date: ___

Reasons: My most important reasons to make these changes are:____

Strategies: I will use these strategies:____

People: The people who can help me are (names and how they can help):___

Signs of success: I will know my plan is working if: (indicate notable signs)___

Possible roadblocks: Some things that might interfere — and how I'll handle them. (Make a list of all that applies)

Roadblocks:

We have talked about this as avoiding temptations so this more of an action plan. So fill out this plan and keep it where accessible.

Day Fourteen

Remake a list of Pros and cons

It's up to you as to whether and when to change your drinking. Other people may be able to help, but in the end, it's your decision. Weighing your pros and cons can help.

Pros: What are some reasons you might want to change your drinking?

Please check at least one pro.

- o To improve my health
- o To improve my relationships
- o To avoid hangovers
- o To do better at work or in school
- o To save money
- o To lose weight or get fit
- o To avoid more serious problems
- o To meet my standards

Cons: What are some possible barriers, or reasons you might not want to change your drinking?

Please check at least one con.

- o I'd need another way to unwind.
- o It helps me feel more at ease socially.
- o I wouldn't fit in with some of my friends.

o Change can be hard.

Rate Your Pros

Now you rate your purposes for changing and attach their importance to you.

Purpose for changing	Rating
To improve my relationships	• Somewhat important • Fairly important • Important • Very important • Extremely important
To do better at work or in school	• Somewhat important • Fairly important • Important • Very important • Extremely important
To meet my standards	• Somewhat important • Fairly important • Important • Very important • Extremely important

To avoid more serious problems	• Somewhat important
	• Fairly important
	• Important
	• Very important
	• Extremely important

Exercise:

Do well to include other purposes you can think of and assign ratings to them.

Compare your pros and cons.

Is there a difference between where you are and where you want to be?

Although it can be challenging, it is possible to manage the difficulties, find healthy alternatives, and overcome the barriers to making a change.

WEEK THREE

Whether you choose to tackle your alcohol addiction by going to rehab, getting therapy, or taking a self-directed treatment approach, support is essential. Don't try to go it alone. Recovering from alcohol addiction or abuse is much easier when you have people you can lean on for encouragement, comfort, and guidance.

Support can come from family members, friends, counsellors, other recovering alcoholics, your healthcare providers, and people from your faith community. Lean on close friends and family – Having the support of friends and family members is an invaluable asset in recovery.

If you're reluctant to turn to your loved ones because you've let them down before, consider going to couples counselling or family therapy.

Build a sober social network – If your previous social life revolved around alcohol, you may need to make some new connections. It's important to have sober friends who will support your recovery.

Try taking a class, joining a church or a civic group, volunteering, or attending events in your community. Make meetings a priority – Join a recovery support group, such as Alcoholics Anonymous (AA), and attend meetings regularly.

Spending time with people who understand exactly what you're going through can be very healing. You can also benefit from the shared experiences of the group members and learn what others have done to stay sober.

DAY FIFTEEN TO TWENTY-ONE

You Need A Social Support

For most people asking for help can be difficult and it may translate to them not having their situation under control. The truth remains that whether you choose to tackle your alcohol addiction by going to rehab, getting therapy, or taking a self-directed treatment approach, support is essential and cannot be overemphasized.

Don't try to go through it alone, recovering from alcohol addiction or abuse is much easier when you have people you can lean on for encouragement, comfort, and guidance.

Support can come from family members, friends, counsellors, other recovering alcoholics, your healthcare providers, and people from your faith community.

Lean on close friends and family – Having the support of friends and family members is an invaluable asset in recovery. If you're reluctant to turn to your loved ones because you've let them down before, consider going to couples counselling or family therapy.

Build a sober social network – If your previous social life revolved around alcohol, you may need to make some new connections. It's important to have sober friends who will support your recovery.

Try taking a class, joining a church or a civic group, volunteering, or attending events in your community. Make meetings a priority – Join a recovery support group, such as Alcoholics Anonymous (AA), and attend meetings regularly. Spending time with people who understand exactly what you're going through can be very healing. You can also benefit from the shared experiences of the group members and learn what others have done to stay sober.

Here are some tips you can use to ask for help from anyone:

1. Write a letter or an email

You will be shocked at how many people would want to support you. As part of this week's exercise write a letter or send an email one each day to potential supporters, it may be to an online mentor, a religious leader, a role mother, or even your parents. The idea is to let your request out.

2. Ask for help from a medical professional

A drinking problem is a medical condition. Maybe it is called alcoholism or alcohol abuse, but sometimes a medical intervention might be a helpful solution and just the right step in the right direction. Book an appointment today with a professional to start your life-changing experience.

3. Talk to someone you trust

There is a level of satisfaction you get from knowing that someone is on your side and is willing to stand by your side through the hard times. Just having someone you can talk to will go a long way in helping you in achieving your drinking goals. Vulnerability comes from trust. There is a level of trust you have for a person or group of persons you are vulnerable bought to share some of your worst secrets with the having the confidence that there are no judgments, of your weaknesses won't be used against you in the future.

4. Look for people with similar issues or who has had a previous experience:

One who has been through a similar struggle as yours and has come out on the other side strong will always have a bit of better and first-hand advice. They likely remember what it was like to be where you are and will do what they can to ease your fears. You can ask them what worked for them and try to determine whether the same course of action would work well for you.

WEEK FOUR

Marie has a made couple of good friends at her regular AA meetings- she needed to attend and her attendance was sent to her company- this and one of the many other requirements were to be fulfilled to keep her job and the contract. They were all the terms and conditions she accepted when the contract was awarded to her.

One of the days she was running late for her meetings. It was a weekday and she had closed late from work. She approached the bus station, and it took her over thirty minutes to get a taxi. Halfway into the journey, the driver realized he had a flat tyre and had to stop to fix it. By now Marie was already fuming with rage and cursing under her breath.

She felt like crying because her job depended on her attendance at these meeting, trying to figure out a solution she searched through her bag, and just as she was about to call Sophie to come to pick her up a neat Mercedes pulled up just after where her taxi was parked and asked if she wanted a lift. Marie did not know the stranger and did not even think twice about the offer, she just hopped in the car.

Charles was all shades of charming, from his neat and well-groomed haircut to his dress sense down to his taste in music — one need not to the told that he came from affluence. He asked her where she was heading to and she gave him the address. Coincidentally, the conference hall used for the meeting was not far from his destination.

Throughout the journey, they talked a lot about work and music. She tried as much as she can to avoid discussions concerning where she was going and her challenge. She considered it to be a turn-off. In less than 15 minutes, they arrived at her destination and she was very grateful and happy for this miracle. They exchanged numbers and he offered to come to pick her up after she was done. Marie was so charmed by this young man that deep down she wanted to see him again so she obliged his request.

> *— One hour later, they were in a lounge where he just finished meeting his client -*

The waiter approached them to take their offer and she opted for water only, there were lots of spirits on the menu and she started feeling sad that she couldn't have one. It got worse when her date requested an alcoholic drink. She immediately excused herself and went to the ladies, where she tried to calm her nerves and practice her breathing exercise.

Charles was still at the table waiting for her as she stayed for so long. When she finally got back to the table, she apologizes for taking so much time- by then, their order had arrived and she was surprised to notice that Charles had changed his order to a non-alcoholic beverage. She was taking a back for a moment and had to ask why he changed his order.

He didn't want her to feel embarrassed as it was just the first time getting to know each other, but she insisted and he gave in. He explained that he noticed her reaction when he placed his order and when she excused herself to use the ladies her AA card fell. At this point, he handed her over the card. Marie looked flushed and embarrassed but he tried to calm her down and explain that he understands and will do all he can to support her.

In the next couple of days, we will try to build our Refusal skills and learn exercises that will help keep our urge at bay.

Not anymore!

DAY TWENTY-TWO TO TWENTY-FOUR

Building your drinking refusal Skill

Drinking Refusal Self-Efficacy Questionnaire

Direction:

The following questions ask you to describe your ability to handle drinking situations. Your answers will be your skill assessment so do well to answer as honestly as you can. The following pages contain a list of situations in which people may find themselves drinking alcohol. Please circle the number beside each statement that best describes how much you could resist drinking in each case.

I am very sure I could NOT resist drinking	I am most likely would NOT resist drinking	I probably could NOT resist drinking	I probably could resist drinking	I most likely could resist drinking	I am very sure I could resist drinking
1	2	3	4	5	6

1.   When I am watching TV   1 2 3 4 5 6

2   When I am angry   1 2 3 4 5 6

3   When I am having lunch   1 2 3 4 5 6

4   When I am at a party   1 2 3 4 5 6

5   When I am on my way home from work   1 2 3 4 5 6

6   When someone offers me a drink   1 2 3 4 5 6

7   When I feel frustrated   1 2 3 4 5 6

8   When my partner is drinking   1 2 3 4 5 6

9   When I am worried   1 2 3 4 5 6

10	When I am by myself	1	2	3	4	5	6
11	When my friends are drinking	1	2	3	4	5	6
12	When I feel upset	1	2	3	4	5	6
13	When I have just finished playing sport	1	2	3	4	5	6
14	When I am at a nightclub or concert	1	2	3	4	5	6
15	When I am feeling down	1	2	3	4	5	6
16	When I first arrive home	1	2	3	4	5	6
17	When I feel nervous	1	2	3	4	5	6
18	When I feel sad	1	2	3	4	5	6
19	When I am listening to music or reading	1	2	3	4	5	6

The above is a drinking refusal questionnaire and it will help you determine how you react to alcohol and situations that predispose you to drink. It will help you evaluate where you are at the moment with refusal.

Humans and then women are by nature social beings and being offered drinks in a social gathering will certainly occur, but developing a refusal skill will help you to stay at bay and not give in to temptations.

Below are some ways to help build your refusal skills

1. Know when to say "No":

Always be clear and assertive without hesitation. Many times a convincing "no" may suffice other times a tougher approach is required, In this case, don't flinch, maintain eye contact and be firm when declining an invitation to drink.

2. Suggesting alternatives to drinking: When hanging out with friends chose a location with fewer tendencies of assessing alcohol. For example, you can choose restaurants that are close to the playground or a school because these locations are less likely to stuck alcohol. Also, when placing your order it is always better to opt for a non-alcoholic beverage.

Practice:

1. Above is a drinking refusal skill efficacy questionnaire, fill it honestly by following the directions on the top of the

form. This will give you a guide on how to set your strategies and where you are at the moment.

2. Now that you've seen some refusal techniques, take out time to come up with one or two techniques peculiar to you. For each day, come up with two (2) new approaches you would employ in refusing a drink and try to use them as often as possible.

DAY TWENTY-FIVE AND TWENTY-SIX

Practice 'Urge surfing'

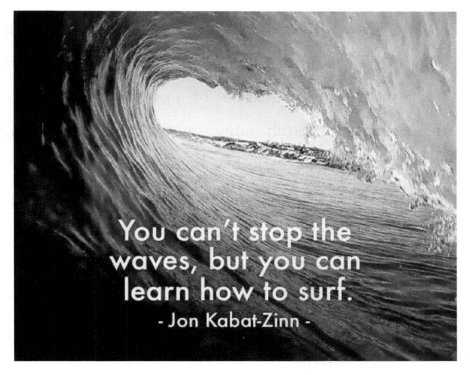

Urge surfing has been proven to help break unhelpful habits and we will employ this with drinking habits.

what is urge surfing and how it works?

The term "Urge surfing" was coined by clinical psychologist Alan Marlatt in his book In his book, *Relapse Prevention: Maintenance Strategies in the Treatment of Addictive Behaviors* (first published in 1985 and revised in 2005). He described urge surfing as an imaging technique used in helping clients gain control over impulses to use drugs or alcohol.

The technique involves first teaching the client to label internal sensations and cognitive preoccupations as an urge, after which they strive to foster an attitude of detachment from that urge.

Cravings are always temporary and that is why this technique proves helpful. Although the time it takes for an urge to last varies depending on the type of craving and the coping mechanism, most research suggests that the urge tends to subside after 30minutes. Another noteworthy fact is that each time you outlast a craving, the less frequent and intense it becomes in the future.

Steps to Surf urging

Carefully follow the steps below to get your urge under control, try this for these few days and watch yourself getting control.

Step 1: Accept that urges will occur

"The focus is on identifying and accepting the urge, not acting on the urge or attempting to fight it."

— Alan Marlatt

Below is a 3-way step to accept your urge

- Assess *how* you're experiencing the craving. Sit in a comfortable chair with your feet flat on the floor and your hands in a relaxed position. Take a few deep breaths and focus your attention inward. Allow your attention to wander through your body. Notice the part of your body where you're experiencing the craving and what the sensations are like. Tell yourself what it feels like. For example, "My craving is in my mouth and nose and my stomach."

- Focus on one area where you're experiencing the urge: How do the sensations in that area feel? For example, perhaps you feel hot, cold, tingly, or numb? Are your muscles tense or relaxed? How large an area is involved? Describe the sensations to yourself and any changes that occur. "My mouth feels dry and parched. There is tension in my lips and tongue. I keep swallowing. As I exhale, I can imagine the smell and tingle of a drink."

Repeat on each part of your body that's experiencing the craving: What changes occur in the sensations? Notice how the urge comes and goes. You'll likely notice that after a few minutes the craving has gone. The purpose of urge surfing is not to make cravings disappear, but to experience them in a new way. However, with practice, you'll learn how to ride your cravings out until they go away naturally.

Step 2: Notice when an urge arises (Record your urge symptoms)

Identifying what triggers your urge will help you to be better prepared for handling it instead of engaging in your drinking habits without thinking.

Practice

Try to identify these "cues" in your drink habit, you can even think of others:

Do you engage in your habit at a particular time of the day or in a certain place?

Is there an emotion that triggers your habit?

Does a person in your life prompt your habit?

Once you know how to recognize your urge then you are halfway there. follow-through to step 3.

Step 3: Resist from acting on your urge.

If you followed the previous step you should have been able to recognize an urge. Once you've noticed that symptom, try not to act upon it.

knowing how difficult this step could be you might want to start by delaying the habit, rather than resisting it entirely.

Practice

Once urge has been identified in any of the symptoms peculiar to you, delay the habit for a couple of minutes say five minutes. Next time, extend the time to seven minutes. Then ten and gradually but consistently it ceases to become an urge.

Step 4: Visualize your urge as a "wave"

Visualizing your urge as a wave can help in controlling how you deal with it. Picture yourself on a surfboard with the wave being your drive instead. Instead of fighting it flow with it and watch how it gradually reduces its intensity as it approaches the shore. Visualize this and feel your urge's intensity diminish.

Step 5: Focus on your breath

When you feel your urge intensify, switch your focus to your breathing. Take a few deep breaths, inhale and exhale. During each exhales, purse your lips like you want to blow a whistle so it lasts longer. Do this for 20seconds.

DAY TWENTY-SEVEN AND TWENTY-EIGHT

Find new meaning in life while getting sober is an important first step, it is only the beginning of your recovery from alcohol addiction or heavy drinking. Rehab or professional treatment can get you started on the road to recovery, but to stay alcohol-free for the long term, you'll need to build a new, meaningful life where drinking no longer has a place.

Five steps to a sober lifestyle

1. Take care of yourself: To prevent mood swings and combat cravings, concentrate on eating right and getting plenty of sleep.

2. Exercise is also key: it releases endorphins, relieves stress, and promotes emotional well-being. Build your support network. Surround yourself with positive influences and people who make you feel good about yourself. The more you're invested in other people and your community, the more you have to lose—which will help you stay motivated and on the recovery track. Develop new activities and interests.

3. Find new hobbies, volunteer activities, or work that gives you a sense of meaning and purpose. When you're doing things you find fulfilling, you'll feel better about yourself and drinking will hold less appeal.

4. Continue treatment: Your chances of staying sober improve if you are participating in a support group like Alcoholics Anonymous, have a sponsor or are involved in therapy or an outpatient treatment program.

5. Healthily deal with stress: Alcohol abuse is often a misguided attempt to manage stress. Find healthier ways to keep your stress level in checks, such as exercising,

meditating, or practising breathing exercises or other relaxation techniques.

Epilogue

Marie struggled with controlling her urge and everything she did seemed not to be working at First. The motivation was there but she found herself slacking. She had the greatest support system anyone could ask for and they gave her their best. Her friendship with Charles was one of the mysteries she couldn't wrap her head around in, he was not embarrassed about her predicament and was not also ashamed of showing her off.

It was in one of their outings he introduced her to someone who finally became her partner in helping her achieving all her set goals.

After being sober for two years, Marie had decided to help other women going through the same challenge by establishing several AA meetings across the globe. She even organizes an online meeting and with the advent of technology, she sponsored many mobile applications geared towards helping alcoholic women. Charles was her strong ally and her partner in seeing this come to fruition.

Changing habits such as smoking, overeating, or drinking too much can take a lot of effort, and you may not make so much progress on the first trial. Setbacks and roadblocks are likely to arise, but with each experience and lesson learnt you get stronger. Each attempt will bring you closer to your set goals.

Whatever course you choose, give it a fair trial.

If one approach doesn't work, do not give up, try something else. You will certainly stumble on one that works. If a setback happens, get back on feet as quickly as possible. In the long run, your chances for success are good.

Research shows that most people who drink heavily, even those with alcohol use disorder, either cut back significantly or quit. This is good news because there is hope.